UNION DES

Grands Crus de Bordeaux

15th édition

The ties that bind us

It may be red, white, golden-yellow, or radiated with soft, brilliant highlights, depending on its age.

We serve it, receive it, share it, and make toasts with it, in all languages and cultures, to celebrate promises, the pleasure of reuniting with old friends, and meeting new ones.

We breathe it in and soak it up while contemplating its substance and virtues.

We recognise its aromas which serve as sensory reminders of fruit, spices and delicious notes.

We picture these landscapes scattered with a château, a wood, a village, or a nearby river, where winegrowers have tended to the vineyards since ancient times.

Generations of producers have followed in each other's footsteps, on a never-ending quest to find ways to best express the outstanding terroir.

The result of a subtle combination of soil, climate, grape varieties, and human expertise, the Grands Crus de Bordeaux fascinate wine lovers and professionals alike with their unique character, complexity, balance, elegance, and ageing potential.

The Union des Grands Crus de Bordeaux promotes the fine and exclusive reputation of these wines, by going out of their way to meet wine lovers and professionals from around the world.

Representatives of these one hundred- and thirty-four member châteaux that make up the Union des Grands Crus are delighted to share their passion for fine wine with you.

Ronan Laborde
President of the Union des Grands Crus de Bordeaux

Today, the Cité du Vin is at the heart of Bordeaux's cultural scene. It has welcomed over one million visitors from around the world since it opened in 2016, linking the city and its vineyards.

They came to discover its futuristic architecture and permanent exhibition showcasing the various facets of "wine culture", including the history of wine which dates back thousands of years, the numerous terroirs, as well as winegrowers from around the world who have helped shape the diverse vineyard landscapes.

Throughout the year, the Cité du Vin offers a rich and varied programme consisting of international art exhibitions, performances, tastings, and exclusive events. It also hosts regular meetings with prominent figures in the world of wine.

It is run by the Foundation for Wine Culture and Civilisations, which aims to promote the universal and living heritage of wine. This has led to the creation of high-quality exhibitions, some of which are held in various cultural institutions worldwide.

The Union des Grands Crus de Bordeaux is very pleased and honoured to have been able to collaborate with the Foundation since the Cité du Vin was established. By providing ongoing support, it contributes to the Cité du Vin's reputation as an emblematic cultural centre.

Sylvie Cazes,
President of the Foundation for Wine Culture and Civilisations

LIST
BY APPELLATION

SAINT-EMILION GRAND CRU

Château
Cheval Blanc

PREMIER GRAND CRU CLASSÉ A
Owners: Bernard Arnault and Baron Frère

Cheval Blanc obtained the highest possible distinction in the first classification of Saint-Émilion wines in 1954, achieving Premier Grand Cru Classé A. This exalted rank was confirmed in every following classification in each subsequent decade. Cheval Blanc became a member of the exclusive "Club des 9", comprising the Bordeaux first-growths.

A page was turned in the autumn of 1998 when two old friends, connoisseurs, and lovers of great wine joined forces to acquire this jewel in Saint-Émilion. Bernard Arnault and Baron Albert Frère became the new owners of this famed château. They injected a new dynamic spirit, while respecting the château's history and existing facilities. They also placed their complete trust in the winemaking team to continue their good work. Today, their never-ending quest for perfection calls for enormous attention to detail and precision winemaking that is resolutely turned towards the future. In 2011, Christian de Portzamparc, winner of the Pritzker Architecture Prize, designed a cellar built as a continuation of the château. Reflecting the wishes of Baron Albert Frère and Bernard Arnault, this building is both futuristic and in keeping with the surrounding historic vineyard landscape, which is listed as a UNESCO World Heritage Site.

Winegrowers have succeeded one another at Cheval Blanc for the past six centuries, in the context of a "wine civilisation" some 2,000 years old.

AREA UNDER VINE 39 hectares

PRODUCTION 80,000 bottles

SOIL Gravel, clay and sandy soil

GRAPE VARIETIES 49.5% Cabernet Franc, 47% Merlot, 3.5% Cabernet Sauvignon

AGEING 16 to 18 months in barrel - New barrels: 100%

SECOND WINE Le Petit Cheval

1 Cheval Blanc - 33330 Saint-Émilion
Tel.: +33 (0)5 57 55 55 55

Manager: Pierre Lurton
contact@chateau-chevalblanc.com
www.chateau-cheval-blanc.com

SAINT-ÉMILION

PAUILLAC

Château
Mouton Rothschild

PREMIER GRAND CRU CLASSÉ
Owners: Baronne Philippine de Rothschild G.F.A.

Château Mouton Rothschild is a Bordeaux First Growth with 84 hectares of vines in Pauillac, in the Médoc appellation. It is planted with the finest premium grape varieties in the region: Cabernet Sauvignon (79%), Merlot (17%), Cabernet Franc (3%), and Petit Verdot (1%).

The estate benefits from an outstanding natural terroir, with well-drained soil and excellent sun exposure. The wine is the result of meticulous work in the vineyard and cellar, combining respect for traditional winegrowing methods with modern techniques, involving highly qualified oenologists, winegrowers responsible for individual plots, handpicking, grapes collected in plastic crates and sorted on vibrating tables, fermenting in oak barrels equipped with transparent staves, and ageing in new oak barrels.

Mouton Rothschild has been managed by two outstanding personalities, Baron Philippe de Rothschild (1902-1988) and his daughter Baroness Philippine (1933-2014). The estate is a work of art and beauty, featuring a spectacular large barrel hall, a magnificent new vat room inaugurated in 2013 and the famous Museum of Wine in Art displaying three millennia of works relating to vines and wine.

Today, Mouton Rothschild is owned by Baroness Philippine de Rothschild's three children: Philippe Sereys de Rothschild is Chairman and CEO of the family-owned company Baron Philippe de Rothschild S.A., is responsible for vineyard management, while Julien de Beaumarchais de Rothschild and Camille Sereys de Rothschild are respectively Vice-Chairman and a member of the Board of Directors. United in their dedication to continuing the efforts of their grandfather and mother, all three children are committed to upholding the château's motto: "Mouton does not change". But that is not to say it doesn't evolve!

AREA UNDER VINE 95 hectares

SOIL An outstanding terroir (high-quality gravel with excellent sun exposure)

GRAPE VARIETIES 79% Cabernet Sauvignon, 17% Merlot, 3% Cabernet Franc, 1% Petit Verdot

AGEING 18 to 20 months - New barrels: 100%

SECOND WINE Le Petit Mouton de Mouton Rothschild

BP 117 - 33250 Pauillac
Tel.: +33 (0)5 56 73 20 20

Chairman and CEO of Baron Philippe de Rothschild: Philippe Sereys de Rothschild
Managing Director: Philippe Dhalluin
Technical Director: Erick Tourbier
Sales Director: Hervé Gouin
visites@bphr.com
www.chateau-mouton-rothschild.com

PAUILLAC

13

SAUTERNES

Château d'Yquem

PREMIER CRU SUPÉRIEUR CLASSÉ EN 1855
Owner: LVMH (Moët Hennessy – Louis Vuitton)

An impressive 15th-century manor house – more a fortified farm more than a château – overlooks the Sauternes countryside around forty kilometres south-east of the city of Bordeaux.

This building became famous as long ago as the Enlightenment. Its name: Château d'Yquem.

Château d'Yquem is the result of a mysterious alchemy that transmutes the terroir, expertise, and a microscopic fungus, Botrytis cinerea (found in the region, and, more precisely, in this estate) into a sublime golden-coloured wine.

In the autumn, if morning mists are followed by sunny afternoons with a slight easterly wind, it is not long before pickers spread out over the hundred hectares of vines to pick only those Sémillon and Sauvignon Blanc grapes attacked by noble rot.

Pickers pass through each plot an average of six times during the harvest in keeping with the Sauternes tradition, dating back to the 19th century.

The grapes are pressed as soon as they arrive at the cellar and the juice is immediately put into new oak barrels for fermentation.

The LVMH (Moët Hennessy-Louis Vuitton) group have been majority shareholders of this Premier Cru Classé Supérieur in the 1855 classification since 1999, and Pierre Lurton has been the manager since 2004.

Yquem's philosophy has remained the same for years: cooperating with nature to produce an average of just one glass of this famous wine per vine!

In certain years, the entire crop is rejected, and not sold under the château name. Nine vintages were not marketed by Yquem in the 20th century. 2012 is the first such year in the 21th century.

AREA UNDER VINE 103 hectares

PRODUCTION 80,000 bottles

SOIL A patchwork of soils composed of alluvial terraces from the Quaternary period with clay-limestone outcrops from the Tertiary Period at slope break

GRAPE VARIETIES 75% Sémillon, 25% Sauvignon

AGEING 24 months - New barrels: 100%

33210 Sauternes
Tel.: + 33 (0) 5 57 98 07 07

Managing Director: Pierre Lurton
Technical Director: Francis Mayeur

info@yquem.fr

www.yquem.fr

 Yquem
 yquem_official
 Yquem_Official

MÉRIGNAC

Ch. Picque Caillou

Ch. Les Carmes Haut-Brion

PESSAC

Union des
Grands Crus de Bordeaux

Ch. Pape Clément

TALENCE

BORDEAUX

GRADIGNAN

VILLENAVE
D'ORNON

CANÉJAN

CADAUJAC

Ch. Olivier

Ch. Carbonnieux

Ch. Bouscaut

Ch. La Louvière

LÉOGNAN

Ch. Haut-Bailly

Ch. Haut-Bergey

Ch. Larrivet Haut-Brion

Ch. Smith Haut Laffite

Ch. Marlartie-Lagravière

MARTILLAC

Domaine de Chevalier

Ch. de France

Ch. de Fieuzal

Ch. La Tour-Martillac

SAINT-MÉDARD
D'EYRANS

0   2 km

Médoc

BORDEAUX

PESSAC-LÉOGNAN

Éditions Benoît France - 41, rue Émile Taburet 89400 Laroche-Saint-Cydroine - Tél. 06 59 34 33 42 - pascal@benoitfrance.com - Printed in France. Toute reproduction est illicite et constitue une contrefaçon sanctionnée par les articles L. 335-2 et suivants du Code de la Propriété intellectuelle.

BENOÎT FRANCE

CRUS DE
PESSAC-LÉOGNAN

Although Pessac-Léognan is the youngest appellation in Bordeaux (1987), it is paradoxically the cradle of winegrowing in the Gironde department. From the time they were first planted to the present day, i.e. for some 21 centuries, the vineyards of Pessac-Léognan have contributed to the prestige and development of Bordeaux wine.

The first diocesan records, dating back to 1382, mention wine production here, including the estate belonging to Bertrand de Goth (elected Pope under the name of Clément V in 1305), which was later given to the archbishops of Bordeaux. Since then, many well-known people have lived or stayed in the region. The Black Prince owned a hunting lodge in Léognan, while Montesquieu, not only a famous philosopher and author of "The Spirit of Laws", but also a winegrower, was undoubtedly inspired by the wines of the Graves – which also guaranteed him financial independence.

The very notion of "cru" and production of the first great Bordeaux wines can be traced back to Château Haut-Brion in the late 17th century. This prestigious estate is now at the forefront of the Graves Great Growths, all of which are located in the Pessac-Léognan appellation.

These estates, members of the Union des Grands Crus de Bordeaux, bear witness to an outstanding history.

PESSAC-LÉOGNAN

17

Château Bouscaut

— CRU CLASSÉ DE GRAVES —

Owner: The Lurton-Cogombles family

AREA UNDER VINE 50 hectares

PRODUCTION
- Red: 100,000 bottles
- White: 20,000 bottles

SOIL Clay on a gravel and limestone bedrock

GRAPE VARIETIES
- Red: 50% Merlot, 45% Cabernet Sauvignon, 5% Malbec
- White: 50% Sémillon, 50% Sauvignon

AGEING
- Red: 18 months
- White: 12 months
- New barrels: 40%

SECOND WINE Les Chênes de Bouscaut

1477 avenue de Toulouse - 33140 Cadaujac
Tel.: +33 (0)5 57 83 12 20

Manager: Sophie Lurton-Cogombles
Managing Director: Laurent Cogombles

cb@chateau-bouscaut.com
www.chateau-bouscaut.com

 chateaubouscaut
 chateaubouscaut
 chateaubouscaut

Three centuries old, Château Bouscaut is located in a beautiful, harmonious setting surrounded by oak woods. The château is owned by the Lurton family, who will celebrate their fortieth anniversary at Bouscaut in 2019! Lucien Lurton acquired ten Bordeaux estates, including Château Brane-Cantenac in 1954, which he handed over to his children in 1992. Sophie Lurton had the fortune of inheriting Château Bouscaut, which she owns with her husband Laurent Cogombles.

Alongside a dedicated team, they make every effort to express the estate's unique clay-limestone terroir. The strength and minerality of Sémillons de Bouscaut combine with the vivaciousness of Sauvignon Blancs to lend Bouscaut white wines their inimitable style. This great Bouscaut red wine, made from an equal percentage of Merlot and Cabernet Sauvignon grape varieties, combines structure and roundness with the spiciness of Malbec.

The renovation of the existing cellars and installation of a new barrel cellar in 2010 have given a new face to Bouscaut wines, and visitors are invited to discover the estate via workshops, events and receptions.

Château Carbonnieux

— CRU CLASSÉ DE GRAVES —

Owner: The Perrin family

Château Carbonnieux is one of the most ancient winegrowing estates in Bordeaux. In fact, Carbonnieux has made wine continuously since the 13th century. The château's imposing architecture, dating back to the Middle Ages, surprises with its understated, elegant style.

The first owners - and accomplished wine merchants - were the Benedictine Monks of Sainte-Croix abbey in Bordeaux who made internationally-renowned red and white wines centuries ago. They also succeeded in introducing their pale-coloured, crystal-clear wine to the palace of the Sultan of Constantinople, labelling it "Mineral Water of Carbonnieux" in order to by-pass the prohibition against alcoholic beverages...

Carbonnieux has belonged to the Perrin family for four generations.

Located on the highest point in the commune of Léognan, on soil that is perfectly drained by a natural stream, Carbonnieux's terroir is especially conducive to producing high-quality red and white wines.

AREA UNDER VINE 92 hectares

PRODUCTION
- Red: 180,000 bottles
- White: 160,000 bottles

SOIL Gravel on a clay and clay-limestone subsoil

GRAPE VARIETIES
- Red: 60% Cabernet Sauvignon, 30% Merlot, 7% Cabernet Franc, 3% Petit Verdot
- White: 65% Sauvignon, 35% Sémillon

AGEING
- Red: 15 to 18 months
- White: 10 to 12 months
- New barrels: Red: 30% - White: 25%

SECOND WINE La Croix de Carbonnieux

Chemin de Peyssardet - 33850 Léognan
Tel.: +33(0)5 57 96 56 20

Co-managers: Éric and Philibert Perrin
Winemaker: Romain Racher

info@chateau-carbonnieux.fr
www.carbonnieux.com

chateau carbonnieux
@carbonnieux
@https://twitter.com/Carbonnieux

Château
Les Carmes Haut-Brion

Owners: Diane and Patrice Pichet

AREA UNDER VINE 29.6 hectares

PRODUCTION 40,000 bottles

SOIL Gravel dating from the Mindel glaciation period on a clay-limestone bedrock

GRAPE VARIETIES 41% Merlot, 39% Cabernet Franc, 20% Cabernet Sauvignon

AGEING 18 to 24 months - New barrels: 30 % new oak barrels

SECOND WINE Le C des Carmes Haut-Brion

20 rue des Carmes - 33000 Bordeaux
Tel.: +33 (0)5 56 93 23 40

Estate manager: Guillaume Pouthier

contact@les-carmes-haut-brion.com
www.les-carmes-haut-brion.com

 chateaulescarmeshautbrion
 chateau_lescarmeshautbrion
 @Carmeshautbrion

Château Carmes Haut-Brion benefits from a unique location as the only Bordeaux château situated in Bordeaux. It is therefore one of the last enclosed urban vineyards.

From 1584 to 1789, it belonged to the Carmelite religious order, which explains the origin of its name. After the French Revolution, it was acquired by the Chantecaille family (a group of Bordeaux wine merchants) and then sold in late 2010 to the Pichet Group who made substantial investments in the estate, including: renovating the vineyard and installing a new winemaking cellar designed by Philippe Starck, featuring the latest barrel ageing techniques.

Les Carmes Haut Brion is a haven of peace and tranquillity in the heart of the oldest part of the Bordeaux wine region. It has an astonishing microclimate that protects the vines from spring frosts and is conducive to early ripening.

Domaine de Chevalier

— CRU CLASSÉ DE GRAVES —

Owner: The Bernard family

Domaine de Chevalier is a very ancient estate, located in Léognan, the capital of the Graves region. It was designated as "Chibaley" (the Gascon word for chevalier) on the 1783 map produced by the royal engineer Pierre de Belleyme. The fact that Chevalier has never abandoned the name of "domaine" in favour of the more recent appellation "château", is proof of the estate's long history.

In 1983, Domaine de Chevalier was acquired by the Bernard family (leading French producers of wine spirits and Bordeaux wine merchants). Since then, the estate has been managed by Olivier Bernard, who perpetuates the spirit of harmony and quest for perfection that has long characterised this superb wine.

Domaine de Chevalier red wine is one of the jewels in the Pessac-Léognan appellation, belonging to the prestigious Bordeaux great growths. Domaine de Chevalier white wine is renowned for being one of the greatest dry whites in the world.

AREA UNDER VINE 60 hectares

PRODUCTION
- Red: 120,000 bottles
- White: 20,000 bottles

SOIL Gravel on a clay-gravel subsoil

GRAPE VARIETIES
- Red: 63% Cabernet Sauvignon, 30% Merlot, 5% Petit Verdot, 2% Cabernet Franc
- White: 70% Sauvignon, 30% Sémillon

AGEING 18 months - New barrels: 35%

SECOND WINE L'Esprit de Chevalier

102 chemin de Mignoy - 33850 Léognan
Tel.: + 33 (0)5 56 64 16 16

Manager: Olivier Bernard
Deputy Director: Rémi Edange
Technical Director: Thomas Stonestreet

olivierbernard@domainedechevalier.com
www.domainedechevalier.com

@DomainedeChevalier
@domainedechevalier
@D_de_Chevalier

**CHATEAU
DE FIEUZAL**

GRAND CRU CLASSE DE GRAVES

PESSAC-LÉOGNAN

MIS EN BOUTEILLE AU CHATEAU

Château
de Fieuzal

— CRU CLASSÉ DE GRAVES —

Owners: Brenda and Lochlann Quinn

Château de Fieuzal is located in the heart of the historic Graves region and has belonged to Brenda and Lochlann Quinn since 2001. The estate has existed for around 150 years.

Combining tradition and modernity, the estate is lovingly tended like a garden, with each grape vine meticulously managed using environmentally sustainable methods.

The renovation of the cellar was completed in 2011. This cellar features a unique combination of wood, concrete and stainless-steel vats to enhance the quality of each vintage and grape variety.

Château de Fieuzal is renowned for the finesse of its white wines and the purity of its red wines, vintage after vintage.

AREA UNDER VINE 70 hectares

PRODUCTION
• Red: 80,000 bottles
• White: 12,000 bottles

SOIL Günz gravel, clay-limestone and sand

GRAPE VARIETIES
• Red: 50%, Merlot, 40% Cabernet Sauvignon, 8% Petit Verdot, 2% Cabernet Franc
• White: 60% Sauvignon, 40% Sémillon

AGEING
• Red: 12 to 18 months
• White: 8 to 14 months
• New barrels: Red: 50% - White: 40%

SECOND WINE L'Abeille de Fieuzal

124 avenue de Mont de Marsan
33850 Léognan
Tel.: +33 (0)5 56 64 77 86

Director: Stephen Carrier

adenis@fieuzal.com
www.fieuzal.com

Château de France

CHÂTEAU DE FRANCE
PESSAC-LÉOGNAN

Owner: The Thomassin family

Château de France is located on the highest slopes in Léognan, on the tallest of four gravelly terraces deposited by the Garonne River over the years when it burst its banks. The sunny microclimate and unusual nature of the soil account for Château de France's unique terroir.

The Thomassin family acquired Château de France in 1971 and continually invested in renovating the entire estate, including the vineyard, vat room and cellar, with one goal in mind: to make outstanding wines.

Arnaud Thomassin arrived at the estate in 1994 and is currently the manager.

Château de France is distributed in France and around the world. The wine's fine reputation is an acknowledgement of its quality as well as the major efforts accomplished over the past 40 years.

The first wine, Château de France, and the second, Château Coquillas, are produced in both red and white.

AREA UNDER VINE 44 hectares

PRODUCTION
- Red: 70,000 bottles
- White: 18,000 bottles

SOIL Deep gravel

GRAPE VARIETIES
- Red: 55% Cabernet Sauvignon, 45% Merlot
- White: 80% Sauvignon, 20% Sémillon

AGEING
- Red: 12 months
- White: 10 months
- New barrels: 40%

SECOND WINE Château Coquillas

98 avenue de Mont de Marsan
33850 Léognan
Tel.: +33 (0)5 56 64 75 39
Managing Director: Arnaud Thomassin
contact@chateau-de-france.com
www.chateau-de-france.com

Chateau-de-France-Pessac-Leognan

CHATEAU HAUT-BAILLY

GRAND VIN DE BORDEAUX

CHATEAU HAUT-BAILLY

GRAND CRU CLASSÉ
PESSAC-LÉOGNAN
2015

MIS EN BOUTEILLE AU CHATEAU

Château Haut-Bailly

— CRU CLASSÉ DE GRAVES —

Owner: The Wilmers family

AREA UNDER VINE 30 hectares

PRODUCTION 80,000 bottles

SOIL Sand and gravel

GRAPE VARIETIES 60% Cabernet Sauvignon, 34% Merlot, 3% Cabernet Franc, 3% Petit Verdot

AGEING 16 to 18 months - New barrels: 50 - 65%

SECOND WINE La Parde Haut-Bailly

103, avenue de Cadaujac - 33820 Léognan
Tel.: +33 (0)5 56 64 75 11

President and Managing Director:
Véronique Sanders
Technical Director: Gabriel Vialard

mail@haut-bailly.com
www.haut-bailly.com

 hautbailly
 chateauhautbailly/
 _Haut_Bailly_

Located just outside Bordeaux, Château Haut-Bailly has stood in the midst of a single-block, 30-hectare vineyard for over four centuries.

Haut-Bailly's reputation as one of the greatest Bordeaux wines dates back to the 19th century and the word "outstanding" most often associated with the château reflects the superb quality of its wines.

The estate has very stringent standards that entail using a combination of traditional and modern methods which respect the environment. A quarter of the vines at Haut-Bailly are a hundred years old, and the estate has a unique terroir resulting in wines of amazing regularity. These great wines have inimitable style, balance and elegance, whatever the vintage.

Château Haut-Bergey

Owner: Sylviane Garcin Cathiard

Winemaking at Château Haut-Bergey dates back to the 15th century.

In 1991, the Garcin family undertook an ambitious restructuring and renovation of the vineyard and cellar in order to showcase the magnificent Léognan terroir.

Thanks to his philosophy promoting organic and biodynamic vineyard management, Paul Garcin's white wine and two reds obtained organic certification for the first time in 2018.

The outstanding grapes reflect the geological complexity of the Pessac Léognan terroir, conducive to the production of elegant wines that express the full potential of their terroir.

Natural, delicate fermentation, followed by long, precise barrel ageing result in vibrant, elegant and complex wines.

AREA UNDER VINE 43 hectares (41 red / 2 white)

PRODUCTION
• Red: 100,000 bottles
• White: 8,500 bottles

SOIL Sandy-gravel

GRAPE VARIETIES
• Red: 40% Cabernet Sauvignon, 40% Merlot, 10% Cabernet Franc, 7% Petit Verdot, 3% Malbec
• White: 80% Sauvignon, 20% Sémillon

AGEING
• Red: 14 to 16 months
• White: 12 months
• New barrels: Red: 1/3 300L new French oak barrels - White: 50% 400 and 500L new French oak barrels

69 cours Gambetta - 33850 Léognan
Tel.: +33 (0)5 56 64 05 22

Managing Director: Paul Garcin

info@haut-bergey.fr
www.haut-bergey.fr

 @chateau.hautbergey
 @chateauhautbergey
 @hautbergey

Château Larrivet Haut-Brion

Owner: Philippe Gervoson

AREA UNDER VINE 75 hectares

PRODUCTION
- Red: 160,000 bottles
- White: 25,000 bottles

SOIL
- Red: Deep gravel with a clay matrix
- White: Sandy gravel on limestone bedrock

GRAPE VARIETIES
- Red: 42% Merlot, 50% Cabernet Sauvignon, 8% Cabernet Franc
- White: 77% Sauvignon Blanc, 20% Sémillon, 3% Sauvignon Gris

AGEING
- Red: 14 to 18 months - New barrels: 33%
- White: 11 months - New barrels: 50%

SECOND WINE
Les Demoiselles de Larrivet Haut-Brion

---

84 avenue de Cadaujac - 33 850 Léognan
Tel.: +33 (0) 5 56 64 75 51

Co-owner – Director of Communications
& Public Relations: Émilie Gervoson
General Director and Winemaker:
Bruno Lemoine
secretariat@larrivethautbrion.fr
www.larrivethautbrion.fr

@larrivethautbrion
@Chateau_larrivet_haut_brion
@chateau_LHB

Château Larrivet Haut-Brion was cited as one of the leading wines in Léognan as early as 1840. The Gervoson family acquired the estate in 1987 and has worked hard ever since to restore this wine's illustrious reputation.

Château Larrivet Haut-Brion is an immensely charming 100-hectare estate. The vines are grown in an outstanding location on tall and medium-tall Garonne gravel rises. The superb 19th century château is surrounded by 13 hectares of attractive grounds, including the Jardin d'Ivresse, woods, and meadows.

An ambitious modernisation programme in the vineyard and cellar has produced wines reputed for their elegance and character.

Representing the upcoming generation of her family, Émilie Gervoson tirelessly promotes Château Larrivet Haut-Brion around the world.

Château Latour-Martillac

— CRU CLASSÉ DE GRAVES —

GRAND CRU CLASSÉ DE GRAVES
PESSAC-LÉOGNAN

Owner: The Jean Kressmann family

Designated a red and white Graves classed growth in 1953, Château Latour-Martillac owes its name to the tower in the courtyard, the vestige of a fortress built in the 12th century by the ancestors of the famous winegrower and philosopher, Montesquieu.

Located on an outstanding Pyrenean gravel rise, this estate caught the eye of Édouard Kressmann, a Bordeaux wine merchant since 1871. He was particularly impressed with the quality of the white wines. His older brother, Alfred, finally bought the estate in 1930. He expanded the red wine vineyard and, in 1934, designed the bottle label with his son, Jean, featuring gold and sand-coloured diagonal stripes still in use today.

Today, Tristan and Loïc perpetuate the family tradition of selecting high-quality vines in the outstanding Graves terroir.

Thanks to their elegant structure and balance, Latour-Martillac red and white wines are widely recognised as among the most dependable in Pessac-Léognan.

AREA UNDER VINE 55 hectares

PRODUCTION
- Red: 150,000 bottles
- White: 36,000 bottles

SOIL Pyrenean gravel

GRAPE VARIETIES
- Red: 55% Cabernet Sauvignon, 40% Merlot, 5% Petit Verdot
- White: 60% Sauvignon Blanc, 40% Sémillon

AGEING
- Red: 16 to 18 months - New barrels: 40%
- White: 15 months - New barrels: 25%

SECOND WINE Lagrave-Martillac

8 Chemin La Tour - 33650 Martillac
Tel.: +33 (0)5 57 97 71 11

President: Tristan Kressmann
Managing Director: Loïc Kressmann

chateau@latourmartillac.com
latourmartillac.com

@Chateaulatourmartillac
@chateaulatourmartillac
@latourmartillac

Château
La Louvière

AREA UNDER VINE 61 hectares

PRODUCTION
- Red: 150,000 bottles
- White: 55,000 bottles

SOIL Gravel and silica with limestone at the bottom of the slope

GRAPE VARIETIES
- Red: 58% Cabernet Sauvignon, 42% Merlot
- White: 100% Sauvignon

AGEING
- Red: 12 to 18 months
- White: 10 months
- New barrels: Red 40% - White 30%

SECOND WINE
L de La LOUVIERE

149 avenue de Cadaujac - 33850 Léognan
Tel.: +33 (0)5 56 64 75 87

Managing Director: Pascal Le Faucheur
Consulting oenologist (red): Michel Rolland
Consulting oenologist (white): Valérie Lavigne

lalouviere@andrelurton.com
www.andrelurton.com

@ChLaLouviere
@chateaulalouviere
@andrelurton

Owner: SAS Les Vignobles André Lurton

Since acquiring Château La Louvière in 1965, André Lurton has worked tirelessly to restore the estate to its former 18th century glory. Château La Louvière became a listed historic monument in 1991 and is one of the most visited wine tourism sites in the Pessac-Léognan appellation. Christine Lurton-de Caix has been the estate's ambassador since 2014.

Tradition and technology combine at the estate to express the full potential of each vintage: La Louviere is famous for its elegant white wines and complex reds, distributed worldwide.

A resolutely forward-thinking thinking estate, Château La Louvière has been committed to producing environmentally sustainable wines since 2010. In 2017, the estate obtained High Environmental Value certification (HVE3), rewarding the efforts made to reduce its carbon footprint.

Château Malartic-Lagravière

— CRU CLASSÉ DE GRAVES —

Owners: Alfred-Alexandre Bonnie, Jean-Jacques Bonnie and Véronique Bonnie-Laplane

Located on one of the region's most beautiful gravelly rises, Château Malartic-Lagravière was purchased by the Count of Malartic in the 18th century. It was formerly known as Domaine de La Gravière until 1850, when it was given its current name.

In 1997, the estate was acquired by the Bonnie family, who enthusiastically set to work making outstanding Malartic-Lagravière wines, considered one of the jewels in Bordeaux. Using a combination of intraplot vineyard management, horse-drawn ploughing, and gravity flow, the estate obtained sustainable agriculture certification in 2008 and became HEV-certified in 2015, reflecting efforts to fully express the terroir. The family and their teams are therefore able to produce complex, well-balanced, elegant, and high-quality wines.

AREA UNDER VINE 53 hectares

PRODUCTION 150,000 bottles

SOIL Gravel and clay on a shell limestone subsoil and clay veins

GRAPE VARIETIES
- Red: 45% Cabernet Sauvignon 45% Merlot, 8% Cabernet Franc, 2% Petit Verdot
- White: 80% Sauvignon, 20% Sémillon

AGEING
- Red: 15 to 20 months
- White: 10 to 12 months
- New barrels: 40 - 70%

SECOND WINE La Réserve de Malartic

43, avenue de Mont de Marsan - 33850 Léognan
Tel.: +33(0)5 56 64 75 08

malartic-lagraviere@malartic-lagraviere. com
www.malartic-lagraviere.com

Malartic.Lagraviere
@vignoblesmalartic
@MalarticLagrav
malarticlagraviere
ID vignobles malartic

Château Olivier
Grand Cru Classé
PESSAC-LÉOGNAN

Château Olivier

— CRU CLASSÉ DE GRAVES —

Owner: The Jean-Jacques de Bethmann family

Château Olivier emerges in a vast clearing in the middle of a large estate consisting of a forest, meadows, and vines. The estate's distinctive architecture, ponds, and attractive outbuildings, make for an outstanding property in a beautiful, natural setting.

Olivier is a very ancient seigneury, whose history goes back to the early Middle Ages. The estate has belonged to the de Bethmann family since the 19th century.

They have invested heavily in renovating the estate in recent years. A detailed soil survey has revealed new potential for the terroir and led the same vineyard configuration it had in the 18th century. Six different grape varieties are grown on gravelly soil atop a clay-limestone bedrock.

Château Olivier was classified in 1953 for both its red and white wines.

AREA UNDER VINE 60 hectares

PRODUCTION
- Red: 120,000 bottles
- White: 40,000 bottles

SOIL Deep gravel, compact gravel on marl and clay, and limestone from the Miocene epoch

GRAPE VARIETIES
- Red: 50% Cabernet Sauvignon, 48% Merlot, 2% Petit Verdot
- White: 70% Sauvignon, 28% Sémillon, 2% Muscadelle

AGEING
- Red: 18 months
- White: 10 months
- New barrels: 35%

SECOND WINE Le Dauphin d'Olivier

175 avenue de Bordeaux - 33850 Léognan
Tel.: +33(0)5 56 64 73 31

Manager: Alexandre de Bethmann
Managing Director: Laurent Lebrun

mail@chateau-olivier.com
www.chateau-olivier.com

 @Château Olivier (Cru Classé de Graves)
 @chateau_olivier
 @Chateau_Olivier

Château
Pape Clément

— CRU CLASSÉ DE GRAVES —

Owner: Bernard Magrez

Few great wines can boast seven centuries of history and trace their origins back to a pope. Elected supreme pontiff during the reign of King Philip the Handsome in 1305, Clement V gave his name to Château Pape Clément.

The present owner does his utmost to perpetuate the ancient tradition of quality. Among other innovations, this was the first estate in Bordeaux to destem the entire crop by hand. The grapes are transported by gravity flow into small oak fermentation vats adapted to the yield of each plot. The entire winemaking process is conducted with meticulous attention to detail.

Combining traditional and state-of-the-art techniques, Pape Clément wines are made to the highest standards.

Everything is done in the vineyard to enable the terroir to fully express itself. In line with the estate's environmentally-friendly approach, chemical weed killers have been abandoned in favour of ploughing.

AREA UNDER VINE 90 hectares

PRODUCTION
• Red: 150,000 bottles
• White: 15,000 bottles

SOIL Pyrenean clay gravel from the late Pliocene and early Quaternary periods

GRAPE VARIETIES
• Red: 52% Cabernet Sauvignon, 46% Merlot, 1% Cabernet Franc, 1% Petit Verdot
• White: 74% Sauvignon Blanc, 22% Sémillon, 3% Sauvignon Gris, 1% Muscadelle

AGEING
• Red: 16 to 18 months
• White: 12 to 14 months
• New barrels: 70%

SECOND WINE Clémentin de Pape Clément

216 avenue du docteur Nancel Pénard - 33600 Pessac - Tel.: +33 (0)5 57 26 38 38

Director of Operations: Jeanne Lacombe
Director of the Bernard Magrez estate: Frédéric Chabaneau

accueil@pape-clement.com
www.bernard-magrez.com

 Château Pape Clément
 Château Pape Clément
 Bernard Magrez
 Bernard Magrez

Château
Picque Caillou

Owners: Isabelle and Paulin Calvet

AREA UNDER VINE 22 hectares

PRODUCTION
- Red: 70,000 bottles
- White: 8,000 bottles

SOIL Günz gravel

GRAPE VARIETIES
- Red: 60% Cabernet Sauvignon, 35% Merlot, 5% Petit Verdot
- White: 80% Sauvignon Blanc, 20% Sémillon

AGEING
- Red: 12 months - New barrels: 35%
- White: 7 months - New barrels: 20%

SECOND WINE La Réserve de Picque Caillou

93 avenue Pierre Mendès France
33700 Mérignac
Tel.: +33 (0)5 56 47 37 98

Manager: Paulin Calvet
Cellar master: Amandine Morillon

contact@picque-caillou.com
www.picque-caillou.com

 chateau.picquecaillou
 chateau_picquecaillou

Built in 1755, Château Picque Caillou is located on the outskirts of the city of Bordeaux in the historic Pessac-Léognan appellation, the cradle of local winegrowing.

A close neighbour of the prestigious châteaux Haut-Brion and Pape Clément, Picque Caillou has stony soil which produces classy, elegant wines with excellent ageing potential.

In 2007, Paulin Calvet took over management and injected new life into the estate. That same year, consulting oenologists Professor Denis Dubourdieu and Madame Valérie Lavigne began providing technical assistance to the new team. Their combined efforts have resulted in a first-class wine of remarkable balance and delicacy.

Château
Smith Haut Lafitte

— CRU CLASSÉ DE GRAVES —

Owners: Daniel and Florence Cathiard

Founded in 1365, this Grand Cru Classé owes its reputation as "the quintessential Graves" and characteristic smoky notes to its sloped terroir containing semi-precious stones such as quartzite and angatoid.

Since purchasing the estate in 1990, Daniel and Florence Cathiard have committed themselves to bio-precision practices which combine innovative viticultural and winemaking techniques with great respect for the vines, soil, and environment.

Organic farming using biodynamic methods and without chemical inputs contributes to the unique expression of the terroir, resulting in elegant, complex, powerful and well-balanced wines.

Estate tours are available 7 days a week and include a visit to the cooperage, 1,000-barrel underground cellar, gravity-flow vat room and Forest of the Senses land art trail featuring monumental art works (booking required).

AREA UNDER VINE 78 hectares

PRODUCTION 125,000 bottles

SOIL Günz gravel, clay and clay-limestone

GRAPE VARIETIES
- Red: 65% Cabernet Sauvignon, 30% Merlot, 4% Cabernet Franc, 1% Petit Verdot
- White: 90% Sauvignon Blanc, 5% Sauvignon Gris, 5% Sémillon

AGEING
- Red: 18 months
- White: 12 to 15 months
- New barrels: 30 - 60%

SECOND WINE Le Petit Haut Lafitte

Route Jean de Ramon - 33650 Martillac
Tel.: +33 (0)5 57 83 11 22

General and Technical Director: Fabien Teitgen
Sales Director: Ludovic Fradin

visites@smith-haut-lafitte.com
www.smith-haut-lafitte.com

smithhautlafitte
smithhautlafitte
ChateauSHL
史密斯 拉菲特酒庄

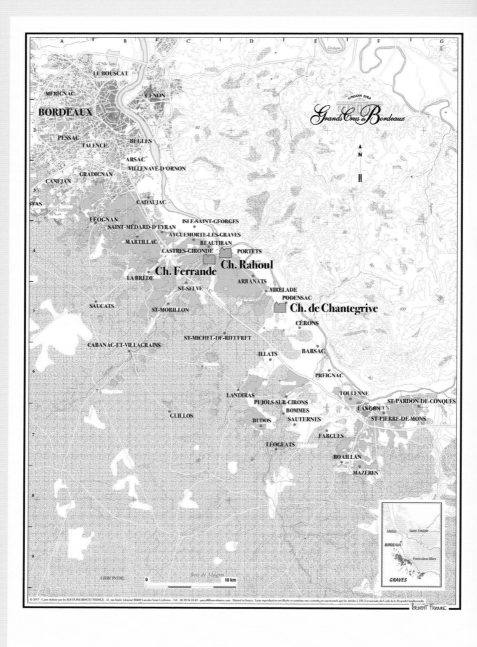

CRUS DE
GRAVES

The Graves region, stretching south from the city of Bordeaux to Langon and beyond, produces a wide range of excellent wines. The Graves were famous for their dry and semi-sweet white wines, as well as their red wines, as early as the 13th and 14th centuries. These were very popular with the English and Dutch, who spread their reputation worldwide.

The appellation is the only one in the world whose name identifies the nature of its terroir: graves = gravel. The soil is ideal for winegrowing, and virtually unsuited to any other crop.

 GRAVES

Château
de Chantegrive

Owner: The Lévêque family

AREA UNDER VINE 90 hectares

PRODUCTION
- Red: 200,000 bottles
- White: 100,000 bottles

SOIL Sandy-gravel on clay-limestone subsoil

GRAPE VARIETIES
- Red: 50% Merlot, 50% Cabernet Sauvignon
- White: 50% Sémillon, 45% Sauvignon Blanc, 5% Sauvignon Gris

AGEING
- Red: 12 months
- White: 9 months
- New barrels: 50%

SECOND WINE Château La Rose Nouet

44 Cours Georges Clémenceau
33720 Podensac
Tel.: +33 (0)5 56 27 17 38

General Director: Marie-Hélène Lévêque

courrier@chateau-chantegrive.com
www.chantegrive.com

 chateaudechantegrive
 @chateau_chantegrive
 @Chantegrive_MH

The history of Château de Chantegrive dates back to 1966 with the purchase of two hectares of vines by Henri and Françoise Lévêque. Today, the 90-hectare château has become one of the most important and prestigious estates in the Graves appellation.

Hubert de Boüard, who also owns Château Angélus alongside his family, ensures the consistency and success of each vintage. In 2017, Château de Chantegrive obtained High Environmental Value certification, reflecting the commitment and efforts of winegrowers to sustainable viticulture.

 GRAVES

36

Château Ferrande

Owner: The Castel family

Château Ferrande is located in the commune of Castres-Gironde, in the heart of the Graves appellation.

The estate is a beautiful manor house restored in the late 19th century.

The known presence of Romans in the commune as early as the 1st century B.C. makes it more than likely that wine was produced there at a very early date. Château Ferrande has been managed by several important figures over the centuries.

The estate was owned by Admiral Delnaud before it was acquired by the Castel family in 1992, after sixteen years of being operated on a contractual basis.

The wines' unique style, combined with a never-ending quest for quality, enabled Château Ferrande to develop an international reputation and enter into the exclusive Union des Grands Crus circle.

AREA UNDER VINE 97.5 hectares

SOIL Günz gravel

GRAPE VARIETIES
• Red: 50% Merlot, 50% Cabernet Sauvignon
• White: 30% Sauvignon Blanc,
30% Sauvignon Gris, 40% Sémillon

AGEING 12 to 14 months in barrel (reds) -
New barrels: 25 - 30%

33640 Castres sur Gironde

Châteaux & Domaines Castel Brand Ambassador: Véréna Raoux

contact@chateaux-ferrande.com
www.château-ferrande.com

ChateauxetDomainesCastel
ChateauxCastel

Château Rahoul

AREA UNDER VINE 40 ha (35 red – 5 white)

PRODUCTION
- Red: 130,000 bottles
- White: 25,000 bottles

SOIL Sandy-gravel and clay-gravel

GRAPE VARIETIES
- Red: 67% Merlot, 30% Cabernet Sauvignon, 3% Petit Verdot
- White: 70% Sémillon, 30% Sauvignon Blanc

AGEING
- Red: 12 months
- White: 8 months
- New barrels: Red: 33% - White: 10%

SECOND WINE Orangerie de Rahoul

4 route du Courneau - 33640 Portets
Tel.: +33 (0)5 56 35 53 00

Manager: Alain Thiénot
Manager of Vignobles Dourthe: Frédéric Bonnaffous

contact@dourthe.com
www.chateau-rahoul.com

 Vins et Vignobles Dourthe
 vin_dourthe
@Vin_Dourthe

Owner: S.A.R.L. du Château Rahoul

In 1646, Chevalier Guillaume Rahoul built a lovely manor house which he named after himself. The vineyards were expanded in the late 18th century by Pierre Balguerie, the first prefect of the Gers department, who turned Chateau Rahoul into a fully-fledged winegrowing estate.

Thanks to English, Australian, and Danish owners, Château Rahoul attained international recognition starting in the 1970s, when the estate was given the nickname "United Nations".

Alain Thiénot, originally from Champagne, who already owned vineyards in Bordeaux bought Rahoul in 1986 and undertook an ambitious modernisation programme.

In 2007, Dourthe joined the Thiénot group, reflecting a major step forward in their uncompromising approach to quality in the vineyard and cellar. The estate has been Terra Vitis certified since 2016, confirming its commitment to sustainable agriculture.

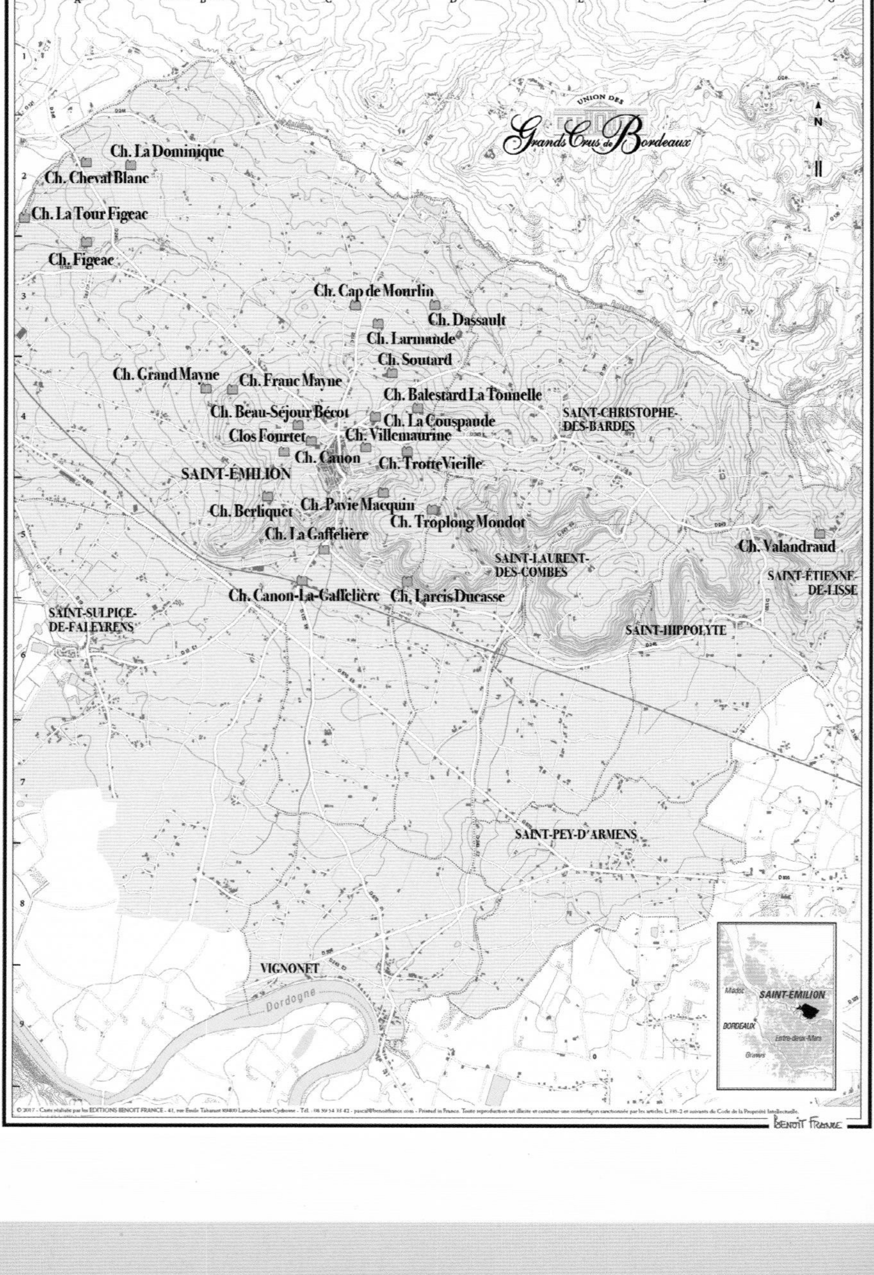
A
B
C
D
E
F
G
1
2
3
4
5
6
7
8
9
UNION DES
Grands Crus de Bordeaux
N
Ch. La Dominique
Ch. Cheval Blanc
Ch. La Tour Figeac
Ch. Figeac
Ch. Cap de Mourlin
Ch. Dassault
Ch. Larmande
Ch. Soutard
Ch. Grand Mayne
Ch. Franc Mayne
Ch. Balestard La Tonnelle
Ch. Beau-Séjour Bécot
Ch. La Couspaude
Clos Fourtet
Ch. Villemaurine
Ch. Canon
Ch. Trotte Vieille
SAINT-ÉMILION
Ch. Berliquet
Ch. Pavie Macquin
Ch. Troplong Mondot
Ch. La Gaffelière
Ch. Canon-La-Gaffelière
Ch. Larcis Ducasse
SAINT-CHRISTOPHE-DES-BARDES
SAINT-LAURENT-DES-COMBES
Ch. Valandraud
SAINT-ÉTIENNE-DE-LISSE
SAINT-HIPPOLYTE
SAINT-SULPICE-DE-FALEYRENS
SAINT-PEY-D'ARMENS
VIGNONET
Dordogne
Médoc
SAINT-EMILION
BORDEAUX
Entre-deux-Mers
Graves
BENOIT FRANCE

CRUS DE
SAINT-ÉMILION

Edward I, King of England, delimited the Jurisdiction of Saint-Émilion, consisting of nine parishes, in 1289. Since then, only wines produced in one of these communes is entitled to the Saint-Émilion appellation. Saint-Émilion's superb reputation is mainly due to the appellation's outstanding terroir, where vines are grown on gravelly soil, slopes, and a famous limestone plateau.

The picturesque medieval village of Saint-Émilion is an architectural jewel, built in a half-circle on hills opposite the Dordogne. The steep, narrow streets, Romanesque and Gothic churches, monasteries, and cloisters make this one of the loveliest villages in France. Listed as a World Heritage Site by UNESCO, Saint-Émilion is an outstanding location which the members of the Union des Grands Crus will be delighted to help you discover.

Château Balestard La Tonnelle

— GRAND CRU CLASSÉ —

Owner: Jacques Capdemourlin

AREA UNDER VINE 10.5 hectares

PRODUCTION 55,000 bottles

SOIL Clay-limestone plateau

GRAPE VARIETIES
70% Merlot, 25% Cabernet Franc, 5% Cabernet Sauvignon

AGEING
15 to 18 months - New barrels: 50%

SECOND WINE Chanoine de Balestard

Château Balestard La Tonnelle
33330 Saint-Émilion
Tel.: +33 (0) 5 57 74 62 06

info@vignoblescapdemourlin.com
www.vignoblescapdemourlin.com

The name of this 10.5-hectare estate has two different origins. "Balestard" was a former canon of the Chapître chapel of Saint-Émilion, and "La Tonnelle" refers to the 15th-century stone watchtower that still stands in the heart of the vineyard.

The château's reputation dates back to François Villon who cited it in a poem that appears on the bottle label.

Ideally located a stone's throw from the medieval town of Saint-Émilion, atop a slope on a clay-limestone plateau, the charming vineyard is currently owned by Jacques Capdemourlin and benefits from a superb terroir.

The wine is fermented using traditional methods and aged in oak barrels, half of which are new every year. Combining respect for the terroir, tradition, and the best of modern techniques, Balestard La Tonnelle produces full-bodied wines of extreme elegance, and one of the finest great growths in Saint-Émilion.

Château Beau-Séjour Bécot

— PREMIER GRAND CRU CLASSÉ —

Owner: The Bécot family

Beau-Séjour Bécot is located to the west of the magical town of Saint-Émilion on the Saint-Martin de Mazerat limestone plateau. It was listed as a Saint-Emilion Premier Grand Cru Classé in the 1955 classification thanks to its unique terroir.

In 1969, Michel Bécot bought the iconic château and established its fine reputation around the world. He also turned seven hectares of former underground limestone quarries into a cellar to store ageing bottles under ideal conditions. Over one hundred Beau-Séjour Bécot vintages are stored there, away from light and variations in temperature.

His two sons, Gérard and Dominique, have introduced numerous technical innovations to both the cellar and vineyard to make the most of this outstanding terroir.

A representative of the new generation, Julien Barthe travels widely to promote the family's enthusiasm and never-ending quest to produce an elegant, charming wine.

AREA UNDER VINE 22 hectares

PRODUCTION 80,000 bottles

SOIL Clay and asteriated limestone

GRAPE VARIETIES 80% Merlot, 15% Cabernet Franc, 5% Cabernet Sauvignon

AGEING 16 months in barrel - New barrels: 65% new barrels

SECOND WINE Petit Bécot

33330 Saint-Émilion
Tel.: + 33 (0)5 57 74 46 87

Managing director - Manager: Julien Barthe
Communication Manager: Juliette Bécot

contact@beausejour-becot.com
www.beausejour-bécot.com

INSTANT BECOT
INSTANT BECOT

CHÂTEAU BERLIQUET

SAINT-ÉMILION GRAND CRU
GRAND CRU CLASSÉ

Château Berliquet

— GRAND CRU CLASSÉ —

Owner: CHANEL

AREA UNDER VINE 7.5 hectares

PRODUCTION 30,000 bottles

SOIL Clay-limestone plateau

GRAPE VARIETIES 70% Merlot, 30% Cabernet Franc

AGEING 18 months - New barrels: 50%

33330 Saint-Émilion
Tel.: +33 (0)5 57 55 23 45

Managing Director: Nicolas Audebert
Export Manager: Andréane Cornard

www.château-berliquet.com

chateauberliquet

Château Berliquet is a little gem in the heart of Saint-Émilion.

The House of Chanel, which already owned the Canon and Rauzan-Ségla estates, purchased Château Berliquet in 2017.

The vineyards, adjacent to those of Château Canon, flourish on the limestone plateau above Saint-Émilion. Merlot and Cabernet Franc vines are planted on 10 hectares, at the top of the western slope of Saint-Émilion, gradually dropping towards the Dordogne valley.

Château Canon

— PREMIER GRAND CRU CLASSÉ —

Owner: CHANEL

Nestled in the Saint Émilion limestone plateau, Château Canon is an emblematic estate that benefits from an outstanding terroir, which entitled it to Premier Grand Crus Classé status in 1954.

The château overlooks a gentle slope where vines have been grown for thousands of years. The vineyard is surrounded by walls that stretch as far as the Saint Émilion village.

The enthusiastic winemaking team does their utmost to reflect Canon's superb terroir and produce wines of great finesse and complexity.

In keeping with the House of Chanel, who have owned the château since 1996, Château Canon epitomises a style that is timeless, elegant and always fashionable.

AREA UNDER VINE 34 hectares (24 hectares designated to Château Canon, Premier Grand Cru Classé
10 hectares designated to Croix Canon, the second wine of Château Canon)

PRODUCTION 80,000 bottles

SOIL Clay-limestone plateau

GRAPE VARIETIES 70% Merlot, 30% Cabernet Franc

AGEING 18 months - New barrels: 70%

SECOND WINE Croix Canon

Route du milieu
Lieu-dit Saint Martin
33330 Saint-Émilion
Tel.: +33 (0)5 57 55 23 45

Managing Director: Nicolas Audebert
Export Managers: Andréane Gornard - Jean-Basile Roland

contact@chateaucanon.com
www.chateaucanon.com

 chateaucanonofficial

Château
Canon La Gaffelière

— **PREMIER GRAND CRU CLASSÉ** —

Owners: Counts von Neipperg

AREA UNDER VINE 19.5 hectares

PRODUCTION 70,000 bottles

SOIL Clay-limestone and clay-sand soil at the foot of the slope

GRAPE VARIETIES 50% Merlot, 40% Cabernet Franc, 10% Cabernet Sauvignon

AGEING 15 to 18 months depending on the vintage - New barrels: 50-80% depending on the vintage

SECOND WINE Les Hauts de Canon La Gaffelière

33330 Saint-Émilion
Tel.: +33 (0)5 57 24 71 33

Manager: Count Stephan von Neipperg

info@neipperg.com
Site web : www.neipperg.com

f @neipperg.france
◎ @neipperg.france
✈ @neipperg_france

Located on the famous slope (and the foot of the slope) south of the medieval village of Saint-Émilion, Château Canon La Gaffelière has belonged to the Counts von Neipperg since 1971. The terroir consists of clay-limestone and clay-sand soil that is particularly efficient at capturing and retaining heat. The choice of grape varieties is rather atypical for the appellation in light of the soil, characterised by an almost perfect 50/50 divide between Merlot and Cabernet.

The estate, which has been certified organic since the 2014 vintage, produces well-focussed, well-structured, complex, and unfailingly elegant wines, which reflect the uncompromising way in which they are made.

Representing some eight centuries of family winegrowing traditions, Count Stephan von Neipperg has succeeded in transforming Château Canon La Gaffelière into one of the leading Saint-Émilion Grands Crus Classés, thanks to a winegrowing philosophy that gives priority to respect for the estate's outstanding terroir.

Château
Cap de Mourlin

— GRAND CRU CLASSÉ —

Owner: Jacques Capdemourlin

The Capdemourlin family has owned vineyards in Saint-Émilion for four centuries, as attested by a wine sales contract dating from 1647. In an unusual departure from practices at the time, this document mentions the place name of the vineyard and the name of the wine, one of the oldest in Saint-Émilion.

In 1983, Jacques Capdemourlin, the present owner, reunited the estate. He also undertook a major renovation in order to introduce modern techniques to ferment and age the wine, including installing a vat room, air-conditioned area for malolactic fermentation and barrel ageing cellar.

The 14-hectare estate is ideally located on slopes north of the town of Saint-Émilion, where it benefits from a clay-limestone and clay-siliceous terroir. Château Cap de Mourlin wine is both generous and extremely elegant, with a very expressive bouquet. It is one of the most highly-reputed wines of Saint-Émilion.

AREA UNDER VINE 14 hectares

PRODUCTION 70,000 bottles

SOIL Clay-limestone and clay-siliceous

GRAPE VARIETIES 65% Merlot, 25% Cabernet Franc, 10% Cabernet Sauvignon

AGEING 15 to 18 months - New barrels: 50%

SECOND WINE Capitan de Mourlin

—•—

33330 Saint-Émilion
Tel.: +33 (0) 5 57 74 62 06

info@vignoblescapdemourlin.com
www.vignoblescapdemourlin.com

Château La Couspaude

— GRAND CRU CLASSÉ —

Owner: The Aubert family

AREA UNDER VINE 7 hectares

PRODUCTION 36,000 bottles

SOIL Clay-limestone

GRAPE VARIETIES 75% Merlot, 20% Cabernet Franc, 5% Cabernet Sauvignon

AGEING 18 months - New barrels: 80%

Château La Couspaude BP 40
33330 Saint-Émilion
Tel.: +33 (0)5 57 40 15 76

vignobles.aubert@wanadoo.fr
www.aubert-vignobles.com

f **Aubert.Vignobles**
🐦 **VignoblesAubert**

Château La Couspaude is located in the heart of Saint-Émilion, near the famous monolithic church carved out of solid rock. La Couspaude has been the pride and joy of the Aubert family (who also own other estates in the region) for over a century. The Auberts have been making fine wine in Bordeaux for over two centuries and have maintained the family tradition of quality and respect for the terroir to the present day.

La Couspaude, was called "La Croix Paute" in the Middle Ages in reference to the cross that still marks the intersection of two roads in front of the estate, and which served as a meeting point for pilgrims on their way to Santiago de Compostela.

Entirely surrounded by walls, like all of the village's most ancient vineyards, the estate is situated on the Saint-Émilion limestone plateau.

Château La Couspaude also has underground cellars where the wine is fermented and aged in barrels, as well as a magnificent reception room.

Château Dassault

— **GRAND CRU CLASSÉ** —

SAINT-ÉMILION GRAND CRU

CHATEAU DA.S.SAULT

GRAND CRU CLASSÉ   DASSAULT

Owner: Dassault Wine Estates

Since Marcel Dassault purchased the former Château Couperie in 1955, it has flourished on an ongoing basis. Major investments are made regularly to enhance the vineyard and improve fermentation and ageing facilities.

Great wines grow out of dedication but also with hard work from one vintage to the next.

Combining great respect for the terroir and 1,000-year old expertise, the aim is to exalt tremendous potential with due humility to the caprices of Mother Nature.

As with any business, a willingness to take risks, investments and innovation are the keys to success.

A perfect balance between tradition and progress enables the wines to evolve while remaining true to their intrinsic characteristics.

AREA UNDER VINE 24 hectares

PRODUCTION 65,000 bottles

SOIL Ancient sand deposits and sand on a clay subsoil with traces of ironpan

GRAPE VARIETIES 75% Merlot, 20% Cabernet Franc, 5% Cabernet Sauvignon

AGEING 70% new barrels, 30% barrels used previously for one vintage
14 to 18 months depending on the plot

SECOND WINE D de Dassault

Dassault Wine Estates - Château Dassault
33330 Saint-Émilion
Tel.: +33 (0)5 57 55 10 00

President: Laurent Dassault
Vice-president: Laurence Brun
General Director: Romain Depons

contact@dassaultwineestates.com
www.dassaultwineestates.com

 Dassault Wine Estates

Château La Dominique

— GRAND CRU CLASSÉ —

Owner: The Fayat family

AREA UNDER VINE 29 hectares

PRODUCTION 80,000 bottles

SOIL Clay-gravel, clay-limestone and sand on a clay subsoil

GRAPE VARIETIES 89% Merlot, 8% Cabernet Franc, 3% Cabernet Sauvignon

AGEING 16 months - New barrels: 60%

SECOND WINE Relais de La Dominique

Lieu-dit La Dominique - 33330 Saint-Émilion
Tel.: +33 (0)5 57 51 31 36

Managing Director: Gwendeline Lucas

contact@vignobles.fayat.com
www.chateau-ladominique.com

 @ChateauLaDominique
 @chateau_ladominique
 @VignoblesFayat

Château La Dominique is superbly located in the northwest part of Saint-Émilion next to the Pomerol appellation and has been producing wine since the 16th century. Acquired by Clément Fayat in 1969, the estate has undergone continuous improvements ever since.

La Dominique has 29 hectares of vines grown on a remarkable terroir adjoining the region's most famous vineyards: Cheval Blanc, Figeac, La Conseillante, and L'Évangile. The clay-gravel and clay-limestone soils give tension, finesse and minerality to the Merlot, Cabernet Franc and Sauvignon Blanc grapes planted there.

The team work meticulously in the vineyard down to the final blend to produce generous wines with well-focussed, silky tannins in state-of-the-art facilities designed by Jean Nouvel. Inaugurated in 2014, the new building features a wine cellar and visitor reception area, and affords a magnificent view of the surrounding vineyards!

Château-Figeac

— PREMIER GRAND CRU CLASSÉ —

Owner: The Manoncourt family

Château-Figeac, a Saint-Émilion Premier Grand Cru Classé, has belonged to the Manoncourt family for over 125 years. This estate, one of the most prestigious in Bordeaux, includes a 16th century château, 14 hectares of grounds and 40 hectares of vines in a single block.

The château's reputation is the result of its fabulous terroir, consisting of three gravelly rises that account for the highest proportion of Cabernet on the Right Bank.

Château-Figeac produces three elegant and well-balanced wines, each with a distinctive character. Thierry Manoncourt succeeded in perfecting the Figeac style. Today, the estate has been given a new impetus thanks to an ambitious renovation programme including new winemaking and hospitality facilities by 2020.

AREA UNDER VINE 40 hectares

PRODUCTION 100,000 bottles

SOIL Three gravelly rises

GRAPE VARIETIES 35% Cabernet Sauvignon, 35% Cabernet Franc, 30% Merlot

AGEING 18 months - New barrels: 100%

SECOND WINE Petit-Figeac

Château de Figeac - 33330 Saint-Émilion
Tel.: +33 (0)5 57 24 72 26

Managing Director: Frédéric Faye

château-figeac@chateau-figeac.com
www.chateau-figeac.com

 Figeac.fr

 chateau_figeac

 Chateau_Figeac

Clos Fourtet

— **PREMIER GRAND CRU CLASSÉ** —

Owner: Philippe Cuvelier

AREA UNDER VINE 18.5 hectares

PRODUCTION 55,000 bottles

SOIL Clay-limestone

GRAPE VARIETIES 85% Merlot, 10% Cabernet Sauvignon, 5% Cabernet Franc

AGEING 15 to 18 months - New barrels: 60%

SECOND WINE La Closerie de Fourtet

---

1 Châtelet Sud - 33330 Saint-Émilion
Tel.: +33 (0)5 57 24 70 90

Managing Director: Matthieu Cuvelier
Technical Director: Emmanuel de Saint Salvy

closfourtet@closfourtet.com
www.closfourtet.com

📘 **@ClosFourtetOfficiel**
📷 **@ClosFourtet_Official**

This ancient "Camp Fortet" (small fort), overlooks the historic town of Saint-Émilion, watching over it during times of prosperity and defending it in times of war. The vines are grown in a single block on limestone outcrops on the highest slopes on the western part of the Saint-Émilion plateau. This unique terroir accounts for the wine's inimitable freshness, minerality, and delicate tannin. Highly unique and dearly-loved, it has been identified by wine enthusiasts as having a Clos Fourtet style.

Since the start of the 1956 classification, Clos Fourtet has belonged to the elite club of first great growths. Philippe Cuvelier acquired the estate in 2001 and handed over management to his son Matthieu. He is continually seeking new ways to invest in and develop his estate, reflecting his never-ending quest to improve the quality of his wines. Their passion and commitment to the terroir is reflected in their plans to convert the estate to organic and biodynamic vineyard management.

Château
Franc Mayne

— GRAND CRU CLASSÉ —

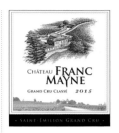

Owners: Jean-Pierre Savare and his family

Château Franc Mayne is a Saint-Émilion great growth, which owes its name to its location adjacent to the prestigious "Côte des Francs" appellation. Part of the vineyard is steep while another part is located on the limestone plateau. An ancient Gallo-Roman road runs alongside the estate. A former coaching inn on the estate bears witness to the steady flow of pilgrims on their way to Santiago de Compostela.

Attracted by the breathtaking landscape, Jean-Pierre Savare and his family repurchased Franc Mayne in February 2018. They hope to give a new impetus to this outstanding vineyard by producing environmentally-friendly wines that fully express their terroir.

Château Franc Mayne is a must for tourists, offering spectacular views over the 2-hectare underground cellars.

The estate is also home to the beautifully renovated Relais de Franc Mayne hotel.

AREA UNDER VINE 7 hectares

PRODUCTION 24,000 bottles

SOIL Limestone plateau and clay-limestone slopes, with clay-silt soil at the foot of the slope

GRAPE VARIETIES 90% Merlot, 10% Cabernet Franc

AGEING 18 months - New barrels: 50%

SECOND WINE Les cèdres de Franc Mayne

14 la Gomerie, RD 243 - 33330 Saint-Émilion
Tel.: +33 (0)5 57 24 62 61

Deputy Managing Director: Martine Cazeneuve

info@chateaufrancmayne.com
www.chateaufrancmayne.com

 chateaufrancmayne
 chateaufrancmayne
 FrancMayne33

Château
La Gaffelière

— PREMIER GRAND CRU CLASSÉ —

Owner: The Malet Roquefort family

AREA UNDER VINE 22 hectares

PRODUCTION 80,000 bottles

SOIL Limestone plateau with clay-limestone soil at the foot of the slope

GRAPE VARIETIES 70% Merlot, 30% Cabernet Franc

AGEING 12 to 15 months - New barrels: 50%

SECOND WINE Clos La Gaffelière

BP 65 - 33330 Saint-Émilion
Tel.: +33 (0)5 57 24 72 15

contact@gaffeliere.com
http://gaffeliere.com

 chateaulagaffeliere
 Château La Gaffelière
 LA GAFFELIERE

Nestled on slopes between Pavie and Ausone, Château La Gaffelière is a Saint-Émilion Premier Grand Cru Classé with 38 hectares of south-facing vines including 22 with Premier Grand Cru Classé status. The vines are grown on three terroirs unique to Saint-Émilion, including the limestone plateau and siliceous soil found at the foot of the slope.

The Malet Roquefort family have managed the estate for over three decades with one aim in mind: to make the most of the terroir by producing great wines with excellent ageing potential.

Château Grand Mayne

— GRAND CRU CLASSÉ —

Owners: JP Nony SCEV – The Nony family

In keeping with the facade of its 16th century château, Grand Mayne exemplifies the values of authenticity and classic simplicity.

The estate cultivated over 100 hectares of various crops in the 18th century, when it was owned by the Laveau family. Grand Mayne currently has just 17 hectares of vines, which have become the heart and soul of the estate.

Distributed in every direction around the château, which sits on a bed of green, over 100,000 vines cover the gentle slope with southwest sun exposure that catches the last of the setting sun's rays.

Grand Mayne is an authentic, yet romantic place, where wine is made with an obsession for perfection and adapted to the complex terroir. There is no need to spell out the techniques - it is sufficient to taste the wine to imagine them...

The Nony family has had the pleasure of owning Grand Mayne since 1934. Jean-Antoine represents the third generation - after Jean, then Jean-Pierre and his wife Marie-Françoise - to perpetuate family management, resolutely turned towards excellence.

AREA UNDER VINE 17 hectares

PRODUCTION 60,000 bottles

SOIL Clay-limestone slope with clay at the foot of the slope

GRAPE VARIETIES 75% Merlot, 22% Cabernet Franc, 3% Cabernet Sauvignon

AGEING 16 to 18 months in barrel - New barrels: 60%

SECOND WINE Filia de Grand Mayne

—— • ——

Château Grand Mayne - 33330 Saint-Émilion
Tel.: +33 (0)5 57 74 42 50

Co-owner - Manager: Jean-Antoine Nony
Co-owner: Damien Nony

contact@grand-mayne.com
www.grand-mayne.com

 chateau.grandmayne
 grandmayne

Château
Larcis Ducasse

— **PREMIER GRAND CRU CLASSÉ** —

Owner: The Gratiot-Attmane family

AREA UNDER VINE 11.15 hectares

PRODUCTION 38,000 bottles

SOIL 10% Clay-limestone plateau on an asteriated limestone subsoil. 55% terraces facing due south (up to 25% on slopes), very shallow clay-silt soil on an asteriated limestone subsoil. 35% colluvial clay-limestone soil on slopes

GRAPE VARIETIES 85% Merlot, 15% Cabernet Franc

AGEING 16 to 18 months in barrel (225 to 500 litres) - 70% new barrels, 30% previously used for one vintage

SECOND WINE Murmure de Larcis Ducasse

Grottes d'arsis
33330 Saint-Laurent-des-Combes
Tel.: +33 (0)5 57 24 70 84

contact@larcis-ducasse.com
www.larcis-ducasse.com

@larcisducasse

@larcisducasse

Château Larcis Ducasse, promoted to first growth status in 2012, has belonged to the Gratiot-Attmane family since 1893.

Upon the advice of Stéphane Derenoncourt and Julien Lavenu, Nicolas Thienpont and David Suire have pursued the family's efforts to produce high-quality wines since 2002.

Their awareness of the outstanding potential of the Larcis Ducasse terroir has led them to undertake precise soil analyses, invest heavily in the vineyard and cellar, and combine traditional and innovative techniques to produce the best possible wine.

Château Larmande

— GRAND CRU CLASSÉ —

Owner: AG2R LA MONDIALE

Grand Cru Classé

✢

CHATEAU LARMANDE

Saint-Emilion Grand Cru

Château Larmande is a Saint-Emilion Grand Cru Classé and one of the oldest estates in the appellation. Local archives contain references going as far back as 1585, where it is said that the jurats, or town aldermen, met there.

Great care is taken in the vineyard and cellar, combining precision winemaking and respect for the environment.

Thanks to a subtle combination of age-old methods and state-of-the-art technology, Larmande makes superb wine in every vintage.

Every effort is made to preserve the grape's fruity aromas to produce full-bodied, attractive wines that express the finesse of their terroir.

Vineyard tours enable wine enthusiasts from around the world to discover the estate's rich history, vineyard, and winemaking expertise.

AREA UNDER VINE 20 hectares
PRODUCTION 70,000 bottles
SOIL Clay-limestone, sand and clay-siliceous
GRAPE VARIETIES Merlot, Cabernet Franc, Cabernet Sauvignon
AGEING 18 months - New barrels: 60% new barrels - 40% barrels previously used for one vintage
SECOND WINE Cadet de Larmande (until the 2015 vintage)

1 lieu-dit Soutard - 33 330 Saint-Émilion
Tel.: +33 (0)5 57 24 71 41

Manager: Bertrand de Villaines

contact@soutard.com
www.chateau-soutard.com

chateaularmande
chateaularmande

PREMIER GRAND CRU CLASSÉ
FAMILLE CORRE-MACQUIN, PROPRIÉTAIRE

Château
Pavie Macquin

— **PREMIER GRAND CRU CLASSÉ** —

Owner: The Corre-Macquin family

AREA UNDER VINE 15 hectares

PRODUCTION 55,000 bottles

SOIL Clay-limestone plateau on an asteriated limestone subsoil

GRAPE VARIETIES 84% Merlot, 14% Cabernet Franc, 2% Cabernet Sauvignon

AGEING 16 to 20 months in barrels - New barrels: 60%

SECOND WINE Les Chênes de Macquin

Peygenestau - 33330 Saint-Émilion
Tel.: +33 (0)5 57 24 74 23

Manager: Nicolas Thienpont
Managing Director: Cyrille Thienpont

contact@pavie-macquin.com
www.pavie-macquin.com

 Château Pavie Macquin
 chateau_paviemacquin

This estate was founded by Albert Macquin (1852-1911) who studied viticulture at Paris-Grignon and Montpellier, and became a specialist in grafting and root stocks. Saint-Émilion can be grateful to him for introducing grafted vines, which saved the vineyards from ruin by phylloxera in the late 19th century.

Owned by the Corre-Macquin family, the vineyard has a prime location atop the Saint-Émilion plateau above the limestone ledge at the foot of the slope. Facing westward, opposite the medieval town, Pavie Maquin overlooks the small Fongaban Valley.

The clay-limestone soil provides superb natural drainage and regular water supply. The high concentration of clay results in generous, powerful, and fresh wines.

One of Saint-Émilion's flagship estates, Pavie Macquin combines traditional methods in the vineyard and cellar as well as a selection of modern techniques.

Château Soutard

— GRAND CRU CLASSÉ —

Owner: AG2R LA MONDIALE

Château Soutard
Grand Cru Classé
Saint-Emilion

Château Soutard is a Saint-Émilion Grand Cru Classé, located close to the medieval town of Saint-Émilion.

The first evidence of Soutard dates back to 1513 with a reference to Bourdieu de Mayne de Soutard ("Bourdieu" designating a Gascon estate surrounding a farm and windmill).

In 2006, Château Soutard was acquired by AG2R LA MONDIALE, the leading social protection group in France which sought to restore it to its former glory.

Château Soutard is situated on a unique limestone plateau home to all of the Saint-Émilion Grands Cru vineyards and is committed to sustainable vineyard management.

The wines produced here express their magnificent terroir in their bouquet, elegance, great finesse, and natural power.

Château Soutard welcomes visitors from around the world who come to discover the outstanding landscape first-hand and learn how great wines are made.

AREA UNDER VINE 30 hectares

PRODUCTION 65,000 bottles

SOIL 70% clay-limestone plateau, 17% clay slopes, 13% sand at the foot of the slope

GRAPE VARIETIES Merlot, Cabernet Franc, Cabernet Sauvignon, Malbec

AGEING 18 months - New barrels: 60%

SECOND WINE Petit Soutard (2016 vintage onward) – formerly: Les Jardins de Soutard

Lieu-dit Soutard - 33330 Saint-Émilion
Tel.: +33 (0)5 57 24 71 41

Manager: Bertrand de Villaines

contact@soutard.com
www.chateau-soutard.com

f chateausoutard
◎ chateausoutard

Château
La Tour Figeac

— GRAND CRU CLASSÉ —

Owner: Otto Rettenmaier

AREA UNDER VINE 14.6 hectares

PRODUCTION 45,000 bottles

SOIL Gravel and sand on a clay subsoil

GRAPE VARIETIES 65% Merlot, 35% Cabernet Franc

AGEING 15 months - New barrels: 50%

SECOND WINE Esquisse de La Tour Figeac

1 La Tour Figeac - 33000 Saint-Émilion
Tel.: +33 (0)5 5751 7762

Manager: Otto Rettenmaier
Director : Pierre Blois

contact@latourfigeac.fr
www.latourfigeac.fr

 latourfigeac
 latourfigeac

Located on the famous gravelly soil of Saint-Émilion, La Tour Figeac was separated from Château Figeac in 1879. The estate has belonged to the prestigious Grands Crus Classés group since 1955, reflecting the high quality of its terroir and wines.

The Rettenmaier family has owned the estate since 1973. The vineyard is managed according to the principles of sustainable viticulture, respecting the natural balance between the soil and vines to produce high-quality grapes.

All viticultural and winemaking decisions are made according to the vintage and, since 1997, upon the advice of Derenoncourt SARL (J. Lavenu).

This very elegant and smooth wine features mint, eucalyptus, and violet notes.

Château
Troplong Mondot

— **PREMIER GRAND CRU CLASSÉ** —

Owner: SCOR

Château Troplong Mondot, a Saint-Émilion Premier Grand Cru Classé, elegantly stands out in terms of its wine profile, vineyard management (the vineyard resembles a garden) and approach to welcoming visitors.

Situated on the highest point of the appellation, this 33-hectare estate, featuring vines grown in a single block, benefits from ideal sun exposure and geological conditions. The unique diversity of the soils produces powerful, elegant, and complex wines.

Troplong Mondot has a rich history, enhanced by the expertise of charismatic, cultured winegrowers whose unique vision has guided the estate towards excellence.

Since 2017, Aymeric de Gironde has brought a breath of fresh air to the estate while respecting its intrinsic spirit and values.

AREA UNDER VINE 28 hectares

SOIL Clay and flint, asteriated limestone and clay-silt

GRAPE VARIETIES 85% Merlot, 13% Cabernet Sauvignon, 2% Cabernet Franc

AGEING 12 to 18 months

SECOND WINE Mondot

Lieu dit Mondot - 33330 Saint-Émilion
Tel.: +33 (0)5 57 55 32 05

Managing Director: Aymeric de Gironde

contact@troplong-mondot.com
www.troplong-mondot.com

 @chateautroplongmondot
 @chateautroplongmondot
 @Troplong_Mondot

Château TrotteVieille

— **PREMIER GRAND CRU CLASSÉ** —

Owners: The Castéja heirs

AREA UNDER VINE 12 hectares

PRODUCTION 30,000 bottles

SOIL Limestone plateau covered with a thin layer of clay (about 30 cm thick)

GRAPE VARIETIES 49% Merlot, 46% Cabernet Franc, 5% Cabernet Sauvignon

AGEING 18 months in French oak barrels - New barrels: 100%

SECOND WINE Dame de TrotteVieille

⋅⋅⋅◆⋅⋅⋅

33330 Saint-Émilion
Tel.: +33(0)5 56 00 00 70

domaines@borie-manoux.fr
www.trottevieille.com

 Chateau TrotteVieille
 chateautrottevieille

Legend has it that Trottevieille (meaning "Oldtrot") was named after an old lady who lived there several centuries ago, who was known for "trotting around". A coach stop was located near the château whenever a carriage stopped there, the old lady (known as la vieille) "trotted out" to hear all the latest news. A 15th century parchment written in Gascon proves that the name was already in use then.

The first wine of Château TrotteVieille has been classified a Saint-Émilion Premier Grand Cru since the classification was first established, with the second wine labelled "Dame de TrotteVieille".

The vineyard where this Premier cru is grown, known as "l'Enclos de TrotteVieille", consists of a 30-cm layer of clay soil on a limestone plateau, accounting for the wine's outstanding minerality, as well as a small plot of Cabernet Franc pre-phylloxera vines.

Château TrotteVieille wine is renowned for its elegance, freshness, long aftertaste, and exquisite minerality.

Château Valandraud

— **PREMIER GRAND CRU CLASSÉ** —

Owner: Thunevin SAS

Château Valandraud was founded by a couple passionate about wine, Murielle Andraud and Jean-Luc Thunevin, following their initial purchase of a 0.6-hectare plot in the Saint-Émilion valley, between Pavie-Macquin and La Clotte. After several other acquisitions, the estate, located in Saint-Étienne-de-Lisse in the Saint-Émilion appellation, covers a total of 8.88 hectares.

Combining tradition, modernity and continuous innovation at all stages of the winemaking process, the estate owners have one aim in mind: to make the best possible wine.

After nurturing their vocation and fostering the emergence of garage wines, Château Valandraud is now a Saint-Émilion Premier Grand Cru Classé.

AREA UNDER VINE 7.5 hectares

PRODUCTION 35,000 bottles

SOIL Clay-limestone

GRAPE VARIETIES 65% Merlot, 25% Cabernet Franc, 5% Cabernet Sauvignon, 5% Malbec

AGEING 22 to 30 months - New barrels: 100%

SECOND WINE Virginie de Valandraud

6 rue Guadet - BP 88 - 33330 Saint-Émilion
Tel.: +33 (0)5 57 55 09 13

thunevin@thunevin.com
www.valandraud.com

 @ChateauValandraud
 jeanlucthunevin_valandraud
 @JLTHUNEVIN

SAINT-EMILION

Grand Cru Classé

SAINT-ÉMILION GRAND CRU

Château
Villemaurine

— **GRAND CRU CLASSÉ** —

Owner: Justin Onclin

AREA UNDER VINE 11 hectares

PRODUCTION 36,000 bottles

SOIL Clay-limestone soil on an asteriated limestone subsoil

GRAPE VARIETIES 80% Merlot, 20% Cabernet Franc

AGEING 14 to 18 months - New barrels: 70 - 90%

SECOND WINE Les Angelots de Villemaurine

Lieu dit Villemaurine - 33330 Saint-Émilion
Tel.: + 33(0)5 57 74 47 30

Director: Cynthia Capelaere

contact@villemaurine.com
www.villemaurine.com

f Chateau Villemaurine

◯ chateauvillemaurine

This jewel of an estate, home to eleven hectares of vines on the eastern side of the Saint-Émilion limestone plateau, combines centuries of history and a promising terroir.

When Justin Onclin acquired Château Villemaurine in 2005, he immediately fell in love with its enormous potential.

The estate's single block of vines is located in the middle of the Saint-Émilion appellation, in the heart of the limestone plateau, atop an extraordinary network of underground quarries.

Justin Onclin's philosophy is based on respect for the terroir and devotion to producing the finest possible wines. The work carried out on the vineyard, alongside the installation of state-of-the-art winemaking facilities in the vat room and cellar, enable Onclin to make the most of this magnificent estate. Long-lasting, complex and precise, Château Villemaurine wines ooze elegance and class.

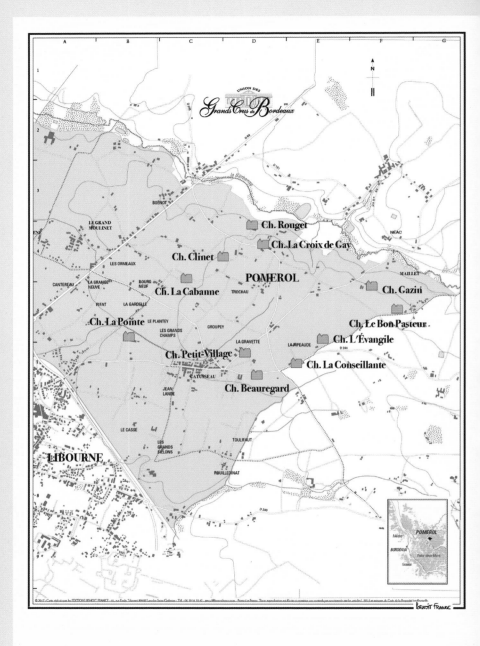

CRUS DE
POMEROL

Located on the pilgrim road to Santiago de Compostela, the vineyards of Pomerol, which date back to Roman times, were developed by the Knights Templar. Although the Hundred Years' War brought only poverty and misery to the region, the vineyards once again thrived in the 15th and 16th centuries, and the reputation of their wines grew steadily.

In the 18th and 19th centuries, Pomerol's borders became more clearly defined, and the rarest wines were much sought after by buyers from around the world.

The major crises of the 20th century were overcome thanks to the devotion and commitment of winegrowers. The reputation of wines from this appellation has increased from year to year. Pomerol produces only a small quantity of wine so, historically, négociants and importers had to go there to sample and buy wines of the most recent vintage as soon as these were blended. This tradition has been maintained at the major tasting organised by the Union des Grands Crus de Bordeaux.

2015

CHATEAU
BEAUREGARD
POMEROL

Château
Beauregard

Owners: The Moulin and Cathiard families

AREA UNDER VINE 17.5 hectares

PRODUCTION 30,000 bottles

SOIL Clay-gravel

GRAPE VARIETIES 70% Merlot, 26% Cabernet Franc, 4% Cabernet Sauvignon

AGEING 18 to 22 months in new barrels (50 - 60%)

SECOND WINE Benjamin de Beauregard

73, rue de Catusseau - 33570 Pomerol
Tel.: +33 (0)5 57 51 13 36

Co-managers: Augustin Belloy and Vincent Priou

contact@chateau-beauregard.com
www.chateau-beauregard.com

📘 **chateaubeauregard**
📷 **@chateaubeauregard**

Beauregard's history dates back to the 12th century. The Knights of Saint John of Jerusalem had a small manor house here which served as a stopover for pilgrims on the road to Santiago de Compostela.

This charming building has been managed by the Moulin and Cathiard families since 2014. These two long-standing friends aimed to give a new impetus to the château and its outstanding terroir by installing state-of-the-art vats and cellars, in operation since the 2015 vintage.

Beauregard wines are grown on a magnificent gravelly plateau and made from an unusual blend containing 30% Cabernet, which accounts for their exuberant fruity flavour, tremendous depth, and elegance.

Château
Le Bon Pasteur

Owner: SAS Le Bon Pasteur

Château Le Bon Pasteur was founded in the 1920s by the grandparents of Michel Rolland and purchased in 2013 by the Goldin Group in Hong Kong, chaired by devoted Bordeaux wine enthusiast Pan Sutong.

Since 1979, Michel Rolland has innovated both in the vineyard and cellar, leading him to become a renowned winegrower, winemaker, and the most famous French consultant oenologist in the world. Alongside his wife, Dany, Rolland strives to showcase the diversity of the estate's numerous soils and highlight the uniqueness and complexity of the terroir.

Today, Michel Rolland perpetuates his innovative spirit and pursuit of excellence as a consultant oenologist at the estate. One of his most trusted collaborators for over 20 years, Benoît Prévot, oversees operations.

Château Le Bon Pasteur and L'Étoile de Bon Pasteur, which have been produced for each vintage since 2013, are two unique examples of the Pomerol terroir.

AREA UNDER VINE 6.62 hectares

PRODUCTION 25,000 bottles

SOIL Clay-gravel/sandy-gravel

GRAPE VARIETIES 80% Merlot, 20% Cabernet Franc

ACEING 15 to 18 months - New barrels: 80%

SECOND WINE L'Étoile de Bon Pasteur

10 Chemin de Maillet - 33500 Pomerol
Tel.: +33 (0)5 57 24 52 58

President: Bernard de Laâge de Meux
Managing Director: Benoît Prévot

contact@chateaulebonpasteur.com
www.chateaulebonpasteur.com

chateau-Le-Bon-Pasteur

Château
La Cabanne

Owner: The François Estager family

AREA UNDER VINE 9 hectares

PRODUCTION 36,000 bottles

SOIL Clay-gravel (blue clay) on a subsoil rich in ironpan

GRAPE VARIETIES 94% Merlot, 6% Cabernet Franc

AGEING 15 months - New barrels: 60%

SECOND WINE Domaine de Compostelle

2, Chemin de La Cabanne - 33500 Pomerol
Tel.: +33 (0)5 57 51 04 09

Managing Director: François Estager
Technical Director: Florent Faure

estager@estager.com
www.estager.com

chateaulacabanne

FrancoisEstager

Owned by the same family since 1952, Château La Cabanne is located in the heart of Pomerol.

While vines have grown there since the 12th century, the name dates back to the 14th century, when serfs lived in cabanes, or huts.

A dynamic estate, Château La Cabanne regularly undergoes improvements, including the complete renovation of the vat room in 2011 following a fire. Winegrowing is carried out with the greatest of respect for the terroir and environment.

Located on the Pomerol plateau with a subsoil rich in blue clay, vines from La Cabanne produce powerful, well-balanced wines.

The wine is characterised by intense, complex fruity notes which follow through onto the palate. The silky tannin accounts for the wine's volume, concentration, and delicious flavours. The long aftertaste culminates in a touch of minerality.

Together with our consultant Thomas Duclos (Œnoteam), we aim to produce elegant, classy wines made with Merlot grapes (100% in certain vintages) on a magnificent Pomerol terroir.

Château Clinet

CHÂTEAU
CLINET
Pomerol

Owner: The Laborde family

The first indication of winegrowing at Château Clinet dates back to 1595. Located in the heart of the Pomerol appellation, the estate was named after the forename of its owner during the Middle Ages.

Over time, Clinet became renowned for its excellent terroir. It was ranked a "Pomerol First Growths" in 1874 and among the pioneering estates to be labelled a "Château".

The terroir consists of clay gravel soil, conducive to growing historic local grape varieties such as Merlot and Cabernet Sauvignon. The vineyard is managed using environmentally sustainable methods with most of the vineyard operations being done by hand. The underground cellar makes use of gravity flow, using gentle methods. The wine is aged in oak barrels and is neither fined nor filtered before bottling.

Château Clinet is an elegant, intense, refined wine with complex aromas of red fruit, blackberry, and sweet spices.

AREA UNDER VINE 11.27 hectares

PRODUCTION 45,000 bottles

SOIL Clay-gravel

GRAPE VARIETIES 88% Merlot, 12% Cabernet Sauvignon

ACEING 16 months - New barrels: 65%

SECOND WINE Fleur de Clinet

16 Chemin de Feytit - 33500 Pomerol
Tel.: +33 (0)5 57 25 50 00

CEO - Manager: Ronan Laborde
Marketing and Sales Director: Monique Bailly

contact@chateauclinet.com
www.chateauclinet.com

Chateau Clinet, Pomerol
chateauclinet
#chateauclinet

Château
La Conseillante

Owner: The Nicolas family

AREA UNDER VINE 12 hectares

PRODUCTION 35,000 to 40,000 bottles

SOIL 60% grey clay and 40% sandy gravel on a red clay subsoil with traces of ironpan

GRAPE VARIETIES 80% Merlot, 20% Cabernet Franc

AGEING 18 months on average - New barrels: 50 - 70%

130, Rue de Catusseau - 33300 Pomerol
Tel.: +33 (0)5 57 51 17 55

Managers: Jean-Valmy and Bertrand Nicolas
Director: Marielle Cazaux

contact@la-conseillante.com
www.la-conseillante.com

Château La Conseillante
laconseillante
@laconseillante

The first recorded history of La Conseillante's name appears in the mid-18th century. It was bequeathed by an influential woman who owned the estate almost three hundred years ago: Catherine Conseillan.

The Nicolas family bought the château in 1871, and its size and configuration have not changed ever since. Exemplifying the family's continued commitment to this great wine, the fifth generation is currently at the helm.

La Conseillante, located in the heart of the famous Pomerol plateau next to its famous neighbours, Pétrus and Cheval Blanc, boasts an outstanding terroir. The wine expresses the full potential of the terroir, gaining a well-deserved reputation for its power and elegance.

La Conseillante's silky tannin, aromatic complexity, and regularity year in, year out account for its loyal following around the world.

Château La Croix de Gay

Owner: The Lebreton family

Château La Croix de Gay is one of the oldest estates in Pomerol. It was first acquired in 1477 by the ancestors of the Lebreton family, who named it after the historic monument of La Croix de Gay surrounding the château.

Château La Croix de Gay was ranked a Haut-Pomerol first growth in the 19th century and its sales price matched those of Pauillac first growths in the 1855 classification.

Noël and Geneviève Raynaud managed the estate from 1947 to 1997.

Since 1997, their daughter, Chantal Lebreton, assisted by her sons, has perpetuated the wine's unique style, which serves as a fine homage to the Pomerol terroir. It was described as a "veritable ferruginous nectar" by the 1929 edition of Cocks and Féret's "Bordeaux and its Wines", referring to the exceptional Pomerol terroir which accounts for the wine's violet and truffle aromas.

AREA UNDER VINE 4.2 hectares
PRODUCTION 20,000 bottles
SOIL Clay-gravel with a subsoil rich in iron-oxide
GRAPE VARIETIES 92% Merlot, 8% Cabernet Franc
AGEING 18 months - New barrels: 50%

8, route de Saint-Jacques-de-Compostelle
33500 Pomerol
Tel.: +33 (0)5.57.51.19.05

Manager: Chantal Lebreton-Raynaud

contact@chateau-lacroixdegay.com
www.chateau-lacroixdegay.com

 Château-La-Croix-de-Gay-Château-La-Fleur-de-Gay

Château L' Évangile

Owner: Domaines Barons de Rothschild (Lafite)

AREA UNDER VINE 22 hectares

PRODUCTION 24,000 to 36,000 bottles

SOIL Sandy-clay with pure gravel on a subsoil containing traces of ironpan.

GRAPE VARIETIES 80% Merlot, 20% Cabernet Franc

AGEING 18 months for the first wine (70% in new oak barrels), 15 months for the second wine (in barrels used for two previous vintages)

SECOND WINE Blason de L'Évangile

33500 Pomerol
Tel.: +33 (0)5 57 55 45 55

Technical Director: Éric Kohler
Operations Manager: Jean-Pascal Vazart

levangile@lafite.com
www.lafite.com

@thedomaines

Due to a curious geological anomaly, a long strip of gravel was formed on the south-eastern part of the Pomerol plateau. Château L'Évangile is located on this rare terroir. The estate is bordered to the north by Pétrus, and is separated from Cheval Blanc to the south (in the Saint-Émilion appellation) by a country road.

The estate was developed in the 18th century by the Léglise family and renamed L'Évangile at the turn of the 19th century. In 1862, L'Évangile was acquired by Paul Chaperon, and later inherited by the Ducasse family who owned the estate until 1990, followed by Domaines Barons de Rothschild (Lafite).

The first manifestation of their influence was a more rigorous selection of grapes for the first wine and the creation of a second wine, Blason de l'Évangile. Plans to renovate the vat room and cellar were finalised in 2004. These efforts have been conducive to a decade of remarkable vintages.

Château Gazin

Owner: The Bailliencourt dit Courcol family

Château Gazin formerly belonged to the Knights of Saint John of Jerusalem (the Templars) and is one of the largest estates in its appellation.

Louis Soualle, the great-grandfather of the present owners, acquired Château Gazin in 1918 and the estate continues to be carefully managed by his descendants.

Château Gazin implements traditional winemaking techniques, including ploughing, monitoring yields, bunch and leaf thinning, mating disruption, and bioprotection methods. The grapes are fermented in temperature-controlled concrete vats. Malolactic fermentation takes place in barrel, followed by ageing in oak barrels. The wines are fined with egg whites, and lightly filtered where necessary. Up to 100,000 bottles are produced annually (including 25,000 bottles for the second wine), 85% of which are exported.

Château Gazin belongs to the Académie du Vin de Bordeaux.

AREA UNDER VINE 24.24 hectares

PRODUCTION 75,000 bottles

SOIL Clay-gravel and iron oxide

GRAPE VARIETIES 90% Merlot, 7% Cabernet Sauvignon, 3% Cabernet Franc

AGEING 18 months - New barrels: 50%

SECOND WINE L'Hospitalet de Gazin

1 chemin de Chantecaille - 33500 Pomerol
Tel.: +33 (0)5 57 51 07 05

Managers of S.C.E.A. and G.F.A: Nicolas and Christophe de Bailliencourt dit Courcol
Managing Director: Mickaël Obert

contact@gazin.com
www.gazin.com

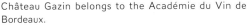 @chateaugazin

@#chateaugazin

GRAND VIN DU

Château
Petit-Village

POMEROL

Château
Petit-Village

Owner: AXA MILLÉSIMES

AREA UNDER VINE 10.5 hectares

SOIL Rubified gravel with quartz and flint on a clay subsoil

GRAPE VARIETIES 75% Merlot, 18% Cabernet Franc, 7% Cabernet Sauvignon

AGEING 15 months - New barrels: 60 - 70% (1st wine)

SECOND WINE Le Jardin de Petit-Village

126 route de Catusseau - 33500 Pomerol
Tel.: +33 (0)5 57 51 21 08

General Director of AXA Millésimes:
Christian Seely
Technical Director: Diana Berrouet-Garcia

contact@petit-village.com
www.petit-village.com

chateau.petit.village

chateaupetitvillage

Located on the highest point of the gravelly plateau in the heart of the Pomerol appellation, Château Petit-Village comprises a single 10-hectare block of vines in the form of a triangle.

Château Petit-Village set itself the challenge of combining traditional winegrowing expertise with state-of the art facilities. Today, the ambitious restructuring of the vineyard and renovation of the vat room and cellar has paid off.

Château Petit-Village wines are smooth, powerful and well-balanced, with a richness and incomparable finesse characteristic of a great Pomerol.

POMEROL

Château
La Pointe

Owner: S.C.E. Château La Pointe

Our mission for the past ten years has been to unearth the estate's history, restoring it to its former glory while remaining faithful to the terroir.

Château La Pointe's 2 hectares of grounds and centuries-old trees have made this an outstanding estate for over 150 years. The château's golden age dates back to the 19th century. One of the largest estates in Pomerol, La Pointe underwent a major renovation in 2008 to help express the full potential of the terroir.

To begin with, a detailed soil analysis enabled a better understanding of the terroir and targeted vineyard operations. In keeping with this sense of observation, the elaborate but fascinating renovation focuses more on the method and less on the means. A major renovation of the cellars was also undertaken, making it possible to ferment grapes from each plot separately to fine-tune winemaking, while respecting stringent environmental standards.

AREA UNDER VINE 23 hectares

PRODUCTION 100,000 bottles

SOIL Gravel and pebbles on the Isle River terraces, clay-gravel and sand on a clay-gravel subsoil.

GRAPE VARIETIES 85% Merlot, 15% Cabernet Franc

AGEING 12 months - New barrels: 50%

SECOND WINE Ballade de La Pointe

18 chemin de Gardelle - 33500 Pomerol
Tel.: +33 (0)5 57 51 02 11

Managing Director: Éric Monneret
Consultant: Hubert de Boüard de Laforest

contact@chateaulapointe.com
www.chateaulapointe.com

Château La Pointe

Château La Pointe

Château Rouget

Owner: The Labruyère family

AREA UNDER VINE 18 hectares

PRODUCTION 80,000 bottles

SOIL Clay and blue clay

GRAPE VARIETIES 85% Merlot, 15% Cabernet Franc

AGEING 18 to 24 months - New barrels: 25%

SECOND WINE Le Carillon de Rouget

33500 Pomerol
Tel.: +33 (0)5 57 51 05 85
Fax: +33 (0)5 57 55 22 45

Director : Édouard Labruyère
Technical Director : Antoine Ribeiro

info@chateau-rouget.com
www.chateau-rouget.com

The first vines appeared at Rouget, formerly known as Rougier, in the early 12th century. Formerly belonging to the Knights of Saint John of Jerusalem (the Templars), Rouget was a regular crossing point for pilgrims. The current manor house was built at the end of the 18th century and remains one of Pomerol's most remarkable buildings.

The Labruyère family, who has produced wine since 1830 in Burgundy, brought a breath of fresh air to Château Rouget when they purchased it in 1992. Jean-Pierre and Édouard Labruyère planted vines exclusively on the upper Pomerol plateau in order to produce wines grown on the finest terroirs in the appellation. With over 18 hectares of vines planted with 80% Merlot and 20% Cabernet Franc grown using environmentally sustainable methods, Rouget aims to be an ambassador for the finest, classiest wines grown on Pomerol's most outstanding clay-gravel terroir.

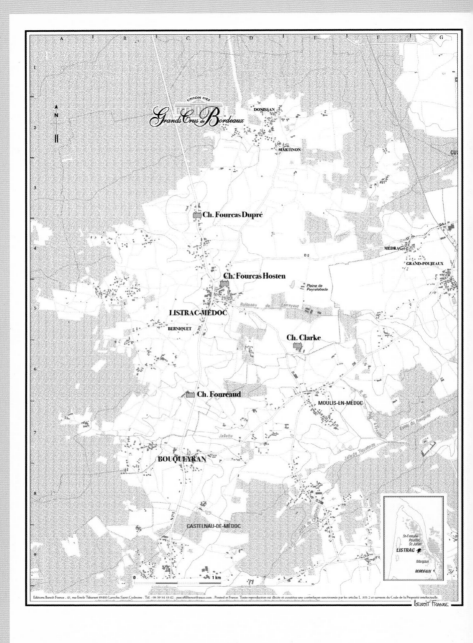

CRUS DE
LISTRAC-MÉDOC

This wine-producing commune has been famous since the late 18th century. *Le Producteur*, a publication targeting the Bordeaux wine industry, noted as early as 1838 that vineyard owners in Listrac were able to overcome numerous challenges to make a name for themselves thanks to the unique quality of their wines.

This quality was acknowledged in the early 20th century when the appellation contrôlée system was first established, although separate status was granted somewhat later than other Médoc communes, in June 1957, when Listrac-Médoc was officially entitled to its own appellation. Three years after Margaux, it became the youngest communal appellation in Bordeaux.

Château
Clarke
Baron Edmond de Rothschild

Owner: Baron Benjamin de Rothschild

AREA UNDER VINE 55 hectares

PRODUCTION 230,000 bottles

SOIL Clay-limestone

GRAPE VARIETIES 70% Merlot, 30% Cabernet Sauvignon

AGEING 16 months - New barrels: 70%

SECOND WINE Les Granges des Domaines Edmond de Rothschild

33480 Listrac-Médoc
Tel.: +33 (0)5 56 58 38 00

Managing Director: Boris Bréau
Technical Director: Fabrice Darmaillacq

contact@edrh-wines.com
www.edmondderothschildheritage.com

edmondderothschildheritage
chateauclarke

Château Clarke is a large estate named after the Irish family who purchased it in 1771. Two centuries later, the estate was acquired by Baron Edmond de Rothschild. Perpetuating his illustrious family's love of wine, the co-owner of Château Lafite-Rothschild, Baron Edmond, had always dreamed of owning a wine estate that he could make his own.

The estate was entirely restructured, renovated and modernised, making Clarke an icon in its appellation. Today, the vineyard consists of fifty-five hectares of clay-limestone rises planted predominantly with Merlot grapes (fairly rare in the Médoc).

Since 1997, Edmond's son, Benjamin de Rothschild's and his wife Ariane's love of the good life and all things excellent is reflected in the meticulous care taken to produce their wines as well as the magnificent gardens surrounding the estate, featuring an incredibly diverse selection of plants and trees.

Château Fonréaud

Owner: The Chanfreau family

Château Fonréaud is a family estate well-known for its historic vineyard and high-quality wines.

The estate is unusual in that its name comes from a legend and also because of its privileged location on the highest point in the Médoc.

Fonréaud, was formerly called Font-réaux, meaning "royal fountain". A legend tells us that in the 12th century, the King of England, probably Henry II Plantagenet, the husband of Eleanor of Aquitaine, was walking through the grounds in search of a spring in order to quench his thirst.

The estate is in an ideal location on the highest point of the Médoc. Thanks to a subtle blend of grape varieties, the terroir comes through beautifully in round wines with ripe tannin that develop wonderfully on the palate, along with fine structure and a velvety texture.

Special care is taken in the vineyard and cellar using environmentally sustainable methods to produce elegant, charming wines that reflect the spirit of the Chanfreau family.

AREA UNDER VINE 38 hectares

PRODUCTION 150,000 bottles

SOIL Pyrenean gravel on clay-limestone subsoil

GRAPE VARIETIES 52% Cabernet Sauvignon, 44% Merlot, 4% Petit Verdot

AGEING 12 months - New barrels: 33%

SECOND WINE La Légende de Fonréaud

Château Fonréaud - 33480 Listrac-Médoc
Tel.: +33(0)5 56 58 02 43

contact@vignobles-chanfreau.com
www.vignobles-chanfreau.com

 @chateaufonreaud
Château_Fonréaud

Château
Fourcas Dupré

Owner: Gérard Jicquel

AREA UNDER VINE 47.49 ha

PRODUCTION 200,000 bottles

SOIL Pyrenean gravel
with clay-limestone subsoil

GRAPE VARIETIES 49% Merlot,
49% Cabernet Sauvignon, 2% Petit Verdot

AGEING 12 months in barrel -
New barrels: 30%

SECOND WINE Bellevue de Fourcas Dupré

Le Fourcas - 33480 Listrac-Médoc
Tel.: +33 (0)5 56 58 01 07

Owner: Gérard Jicquel
Director: Lucas Leclercq

info@fourcasdupre.com
www.fourcasdupre.com

Château Fourcas Dupré
@fourcasdupre

Château Fourcas Dupré boasts 47 hectares of vines grown in a single block on a 42-metre rise nicknamed the "roof of the Médoc", benefiting from excellent natural drainage.

The terroir is an unusual blend of gravel, clay, and limestone conducive to producing complex, elegant wines with great ageing potential. The 80% Pyrenean gravel soils make for wines with strong personality.

In July 2019, Gérard Jicquel acquired the château to fulfil his passion to produce Bordeaux red wines. His dearest wish now is to ensure the château produces wines of outstanding quality.

Château Fourcas Dupré is committed to becoming an estate where wine professionals and enthusiasts alike find a unique, modern place where wine is the driving force of a true passion.

Château Fourcas Hosten

Owners: Renaud and Laurent Momméja

Since 1810, Château Fourcas Hosten has been passed down to numerous generations, who have each played their part in building its reputation and future while preserving its traditions.

Renaud and Laurent Momméja are fully committed to developing the estate to produce wines that express their terroir. Their forward-thinking approach is reflected in the château's conversion to organic vineyard management.

Meanwhile, a vast replanting programme has been undertaken in the vineyard to perfectly match the grape varieties to the soil. Blending two complementary clay-limestone and Pyrenean gravel terroirs, the wines of Château Fourcas Hosten feature a perfect balance between crisp fruit and complex flavours with a velvety texture. The elegant tannic structure accounts for the wine's superb finesse.

AREA UNDER VINE 40 hectares

PRODUCTION 130,000 bottles

SOIL 25 hectares of Pyrenean gravel and 15 hectares of clay-limestone soil

GRAPE VARIETIES 55% Cabernet Sauvignon, 40% Merlot, 2.5% Cabernet Franc, 2.5% Petit Verdot

AGEING 12 months in barrel - New barrels: 33%

SECOND WINE Les Cèdres d'Hosten

5, rue Odilon Redon - 33480 Listrac-Médoc
Tel.: +33 (0)5 56 58 01 15

contact@fourcas-hosten.com
www.fourcas-hosten.com

 chateaufourcashosten
 fourcashosten

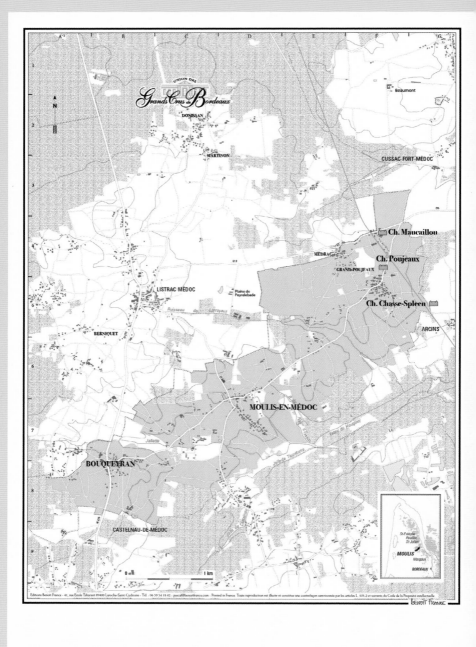

CRUS DE
MOULIS-EN-MÉDOC

The commune of Moulis, and thus the wine appellation, are named after the numerous moulins, or mills (both water and wind-powered) found there at one time. Moulis is a deformation of the words molinis and mola of Latin origin. While this name proves that grain was grown in the region, we also know that vines were cultivated here as far back as the Middle Ages by several vineyard owners and a large religious community. The winegrowing commune of Moulis is probably one of the oldest in the Médoc. Bearing witness to a prestigious past, the town also has one of the most beautiful Romanesque churches in the entire region.

The vineyards of Moulis and the reputation of its wines greatly developed during the 18th and 19th centuries, at the same time as other neighbouring communes.

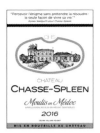

Château
Chasse-Spleen

Owner: Céline Villars-Foubet

AREA UNDER VINE 103 hectares

PRODUCTION 300 to 350,000 bottles

SOIL Garonne gravel on an asteriated limestone subsoil

GRAPE VARIETIES 55% Cabernet Sauvignon, 38% Merlot, 5% Petit Verdot, 2% Cabernet Franc

AGEING 18 months for the first wine - New barrels: 40%

SECOND WINE Oratoire de Chasse-Spleen

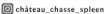

32 Chemin de la Raze
33480 Moulis en Médoc
Tel.: +33 (0)5 56 58 02 37

President: Céline Villars-Foubet
Deputy Managing Director: Jean-Pierre Foubet

info@chasse-spleen.com
www.chasse-spleen.com

Château Chasse-Spleen
château_chasse_spleen

Some people attribute the name to Lord Byron during a trip he made to France and others to Charles Baudelaire when he visited a friend who happened to live next to the château. What is certain is that the painter Odilon Redon, neighbour of the estate and illustrator of "Paris Spleen", did suggest this lovely name to the estate owners in 1863.

Chasse-Spleen has been managed by women for the past thirty years: Jacques Merlaut's daughter, Bernadette Villars, starting in 1976, followed by her daughter, Claire, beginning in 1992, and now her second daughter, Céline.

The vineyard is located just off the Route des Châteaux, halfway between Margaux and Saint-Julien, in the smallest Médoc appellation. The estate features an extraordinarily varied terroir consisting of complementary soil types ranging from pure Garonne and Pyrenean gravel to a mixture of clay and limestone.

Chasse-Spleen's wine reflects this diversity and the best of its appellation combining the fresh, mineral qualities of Cabernet Sauvignon grown on a thick layer of gravel, and the round smoothness of Merlot planted on predominantly clay-limestone soil.

In 2017, Chasse-Spleen became home to a contemporary art centre.

Château Maucaillou

Owner: S.A.S Château Maucaillou

The original château was built in 1875, surrounded by 1.5 hectares of vines. The architectural style is very Baroque, which was popular in the 19th century.

When they arrived at the estate in 1929, the Dourthe brothers, Roger and André, devoted their efforts to expanding the vineyards, attaining 20 hectares in 1967. Thanks to impetus from Philippe Dourthe, Roger's son, the estate expanded with a further 67 hectares of vines over a forty-year period. In 2007, Philippe Dourthe handed over management to his children: Caroline, Pascal, and Magali. A fully-qualified team respectful of the Dourthe winemaking philosophy is now in charge of the estate. Our wines are the result of a meticulous selection of grapes in the vineyard, as well as precision winemaking and ageing. They are appreciated throughout the world by professionals and wine enthusiasts alike.

As forerunners of wine tourism, we welcome visitors all year round to discover the Museum of the Arts and Crafts of the Vine and Wine as well as our state-of-the-art winemaking facilities.

AREA UNDER VINE 87 hectares

PRODUCTION 300 to 360,000 bottles

SOIL 75% Garonne gravel (Günz) and 25% clay-limestone

GRAPE VARIETIES 51% Cabernet Sauvignon, 42% Merlot, 7% Petit Verdot

AGEING 14 to 16 months - New barrels: 40 - 50%

SECOND WINE N°2 de Maucaillou

33480 Moulis-en-Médoc
Tel.: +33 (0)5 56 58 01 23

President of the Executive Board: Pascal Dourthe
Director of Communication: Cyril Forget

chateau@maucaillou.com
www.maucaillou.com

Chateau-Maucaillou

Château
Poujeaux

Owner: The Cuvelier family

AREA UNDER VINE 68 hectares

PRODUCTION 250,000 bottles

SOIL Günz gravel

GRAPE VARIETIES 50% Cabernet Sauvignon, 40% Merlot, 5% Cabernet Franc, 5% Petit Verdot

AGEING 12 months - New barrels: 30%

SECOND WINE La Salle de Château Poujeaux

450 avenue de la Gironde
33480 Moulis-en-Médoc
Tel.: +33 (0) 5 56 58 02 96

Manager: Matthieu Cuvelier
Managing Director: Christophe Labenne

contact@chateau-poujeaux.com
www.chateaupoujeaux.com

In the Middle Ages, Poujeaux was a seigneury owing allegiance to Latour Saint Mambert, the future Château Latour. Winegrowing at Poujeaux dates back to the 19th century. A period of prosperity was followed by a series of different owners and the vineyard was broken up in the early 20th century. Fortunately, it was reconsolidated by the Theil family who did much to give the wine a fine reputation.

Château Poujeaux was purchased by the Cuvelier family (who already owned Clos Fourtet, a Premier Grand Cru Classé in Saint-Émilion) in January 2008. This marked the beginning of a new chapter in Poujeaux's history. Philippe Cuvelier and his son, Matthieu, asked Stéphane Derenoncourt to advise them, while retaining the existing winemaking team. This is headed by Christophe Labenne, the grandson of the former owners.

The vines are grown on a magnificent gravelly rise in the heart of the Médoc. While perpetuating the wine's generous yet delicate style, the new orientation is toward enhanced precision in order to bring Poujeaux up to its ultimate potential.

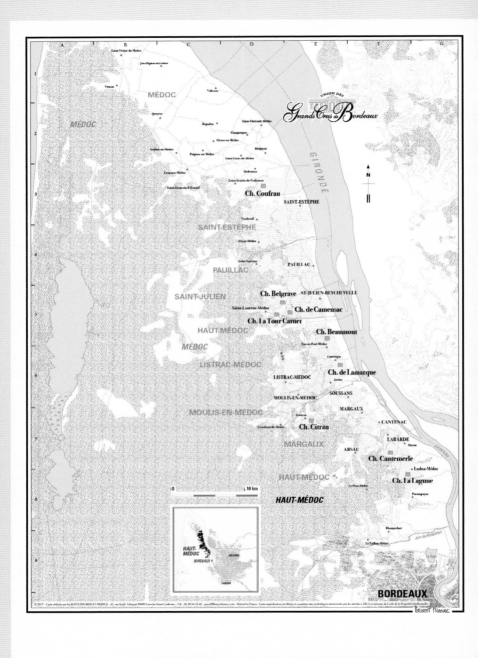

CRUS DE
HAUT-MÉDOC

The Haut-Médoc stretches northwest of Bordeaux, from a stream called the Jalle de Blanquefort to the commune of Saint-Seurin-de-Cadourne. These boundaries had been defined for many years, and wines from this region have a long-established reputation. The part of the Médoc located closest to the city of Bordeaux, its vast terroir has produced fine wine since the 17th century. The owners of large estates made the most of their privileged location close to the port of Bordeaux and major transportation routes to export their wines all over the world. The northernmost vineyards were mostly created in the latter half of the 19th century.

Château Beaumont

Owner: Grands Millésimes de France
(Castel Frères and Suntory)

AREA UNDER VINE 114 hectares

PRODUCTION 550,000 bottles

SOIL A rise consisting of Günz gravel and sand

GRAPE VARIETIES 50% Cabernet Sauvignon, 47% Merlot, 3% Petit Verdot

AGEING 12 to 14 months - New barrels: 30%

SECOND WINE Les Tours de Beaumont

28 Beaumont Nord
33460 Cussac Fort Médoc
Tel.: +33 (0)5 56 58 92 29

Manager: Philippe Blanc
Technical Director: Anthony Yaigre

beaumont@chateau-beaumont.com
www.chateau-beaumont.com

f Chateau Beaumont

Located between Margaux and Saint-Julien in Cussac-Fort-Médoc, Château Beaumont has 114 hectares of vines in a single block overlooking the Gironde Estuary.

The château, a pure jewel of Mansart-style architecture, was built in 1854. Its exotic history includes an unusual collection of characters: a Breton aristocrat, a Honduran minister, a Parisian industrialist, a lieutenant-colonel from Caracas, a Venezuelan senator – twelve different owners who likely ensured that Beaumont was enjoyed around the world.

Currently owned by Grands Millésimes de France, Château Beaumont produces an elegant, concentrated, and well-balanced wine with a beautiful colour, extreme finesse, and delicate flavours.

The estate has been committed to sustainable viticulture (Terra Vitis) since 2004 and obtained the highest echelon (level 3) of High Environmental Value certification in 2016.

Château Belgrave

— GRAND CRU CLASSÉ EN 1855 —

GRAND CRU CLASSÉ EN 1855

Château Belgrave

HAUT-MÉDOC

VIGNOBLES DOURTHE

Owner: GFV du Château Belgrave

Château Belgrave, a former hunting lodge during the reign of Louis XV, was listed in the Médoc classification in 1815 under the name of Coutanceau. Bordeaux wine merchant Bruno Devez renovated the vineyard and cellar and built the current remains around 1850. He renamed the estate "Belgrave" in honour of the high-quality deep gravel terroir, separated from the Saint-Julien appellation by a small stream.

Marcel Alibert, one of the estate's illustrious owners eager to protect and showcase Médoc wines, went on to become the co-founder of the Crus Classés Syndicate and later the Winegrower's Syndicate in the early 20th century.

Since Dourthe took over management of Château Belgrave in 1979, a great deal of work, passion, and energy have gone into producing wines that showcase the estate's rich history and the fine Médoc terroir.

AREA UNDER VINE 59 hectares

PRODUCTION 215,000 bottles

SOIL Deep gravel on a clay subsoil

GRAPE VARIETIES 50% Merlot, 46% Cabernet Sauvignon, 4% Petit Verdot

AGEING 12 months in barrel - New barrels: 33%

SECOND WINE Diane de Belgrave

———•———

Château Belgrave
33112 Saint-Laurent-Médoc
Tel.: +33 (0)5 56 35 53 00

Manager: Patrick Jestin
Director of Vignobles Dourthe: Frédéric Bonnaffous

contact@dourthe.com
www.chateau-belgrave.com

Vins et Vignobles Dourthe
vin_dourthe
@Vin_Dourthe

Château de Camensac

— GRAND CRU CLASSÉ EN **1855** —

Owners: Jean Merlaut and Céline Villars-Foubet

AREA UNDER VINE 75 hectares

PRODUCTION 180,000 bottles

SOIL Gravel, sandy-gravel and sandy-clay gravel

GRAPE VARIETIES 60% Cabernet Sauvignon, 40% Merlot

AGEING 15 to 18 months - New barrels: 40%

SECOND WINE Closerie de Camensac

Route de Saint Julien
33112 Saint Laurent Médoc
Tel.: +33 (0)5 56 59 41 67

Production Manager: Claire Thomas-Chenard
Head of Wine Tourism: Mélissa Avril

info@chateaucamensac.com
www.chateaucamensac.com/

 chateau.decamensac
 chateaudecamensac

Château de Camensac is located on the perimeter of the Médoc's great growths, bordering on the Saint-Julien appellation. The 75-hectare vineyard consists of Cabernet Sauvignon and Merlot vines on slopes with deep gravel soil over a clay and hardpan subsoil.

Camensac is a very old estate that was included on Belleyme's famous 18th century map. In Médoc patois, "Camensac" means "on the water's way" and comes from the words "camens", meaning "path" or "way" and "ac", which means "water" in local dialect. In the 17th century, monks dug ditches along the bottom of the gravelly rises. These contributed to the quality of the terroir by draining off excess rainwater.

The Merlaut family acquired Camensac in time for the 2005 vintage and Céline Villars and Jean Merlaut are now in charge of the estate. The niece and uncle are also the respective owners of Chasse-Spleen and Gruaud-Larose. Éric Boissenot is the consulting oenologist.

Château Cantemerle

— GRAND CRU CLASSÉ EN 1855 —

Owner: SMA Group

Château Cantemerle, designated a great growth in the 1855 classification, is located on deep fine gravel soil in the communes of Macau and Ludon. Thanks to its unique microclimate and soil, Cantemerle produces complex, well-balanced, and refined wines.

After belonging to the Villeneuve (1576-1892) and Dubos (1892-1980) families, the château was acquired in 1981 by the SMA group, a large mutual insurance company for the construction and civil engineering sector. The estate's long history is reflected in the château's distinctive architecture and the magnificent grounds that surround it. Cantemerle exudes romantic charm and the vineyard has a magical feeling to it.

Cantemerle wines are elegant and powerful on the palate and particularly attractive when young. They are made by an experienced and enthusiastic team using a careful blend of traditional and state-of-the-art techniques.

GRAND CRU CLASSÉ EN 1855

CHÂTEAU
CANTEMERLE
HAUT-MÉDOC
2016
MIS EN BOUTEILLE AU CHÂTEAU
— MACAU · MÉDOC · FRANCE —

AREA UNDER VINE 93 hectares

PRODUCTION 400,000 bottles

SOIL Siliceous and deep gravel from the Quaternary period

GRAPE VARIETIES 64% Cabernet Sauvignon, 27% Merlot, 5% Cabernet Franc, 4% Petit Verdot

AGEING 16 months in barrels including 12 in French oak barrels - New barrels: 35%

SECOND WINE Les Allées de Cantemerle

33460 Macau
Tel.: +33 (0)5 57 97 02 82

Managing Director: Philippe Dambrine

cantemerle@cantemerle.com
www.cantemerle.com

🇫 cantemerle
⬛ chateau_cantemerle

Château Citran

Owner: The Merlaut family

AREA UNDER VINE 100 hectares

PRODUCTION 350,000 bottles

SOIL Sandy-gravel on an asteriated limestone and clay-limestone subsoil

GRAPE VARIETIES 50% Merlot, 45% Cabernet Sauvignon, 5% Cabernet Franc

AGEING 15 months - New barrels: 30%

SECOND WINE Moulins de Citran

Chemin de Citran - 33480 Avensan
Tel.: +33(0)5 56 58 21 01

info@citran.com
www.citran.com

Château Citran is one of the oldest estates in the Médoc. The Donissan de Citran family reigned over this former Médoc seigneury from the 13th century until 1832. The current estate was rebuilt between 1862 and 1864 on the site of the medieval château. Nestled in verdant parkland and surrounded by moats, Château Citran is a listed historical monument.

In 1996, the Merlaut family, deeply involved in the Bordeaux wine industry, took over this magnificent estate. Today, Château Citran has 100 hectares of vines in the Haut-Medoc appellation, planted with grape varieties that express their full potential of the terroir, including Cabernet Sauvignon, Merlot, and Cabernet Franc.

The combination of traditional and state-of-the-art winemaking techniques in the vineyard and cellar result in an elegant and classy wine. Citran is renowned for its quality and finesse. The château's logo is a peacock, which can also be found on the estate's grounds.

Château Coufran

Owner: The Miailhe family

Château Coufran was acquired in 1924 by Louis Miailhe. The Miailhe family were well-known brokers at the time, and their experience in this profession dates back to 1793. Marie-Cécile Vicaire and Éric Miailhe now manage the family estates, including Château Coufran and Château Verdignan.

Often called the "Pomerol of the Médoc" since it is made entirely from Merlot, Château Coufran benefits from an outstanding location overlooking the Gironde Estuary, with a mild microclimate and excellent sun exposure.

This large estate produces over 400,000 bottles of generous, concentrated wine that ages very well, alongside wines ready to drink now. Modern storage facilities house large quantities of wines from the previous ten vintages. This makes it possible to appreciate mature wines with an excellent quality/price ratio, and whose provenance one can be assured of.

AREA UNDER VINE 76 hectares

PRODUCTION 420,000 bottles

SOIL Garonne gravel

GRAPE VARIETIES 85% Merlot, 15% Cabernet Sauvignon

AGEING 12 to 18 months- New barrels: 25%

SECOND WINE N°2 de Coufran

33180 Saint-Seurin de Cadourne
Tel.: Château +33 (0)5 56 59 31 02
Office +33 (0)5 56 44 90 84
contact@chateau-coufran.com
www.chateau-coufran.com

f **Chateau Coufran**
@chateauxcoufranverdignan

GRAND CRU CLASSÉ

CHATEAU LA LAGUNE

2015

HAUT-MÉDOC

Château
La Lagune

— GRAND CRU CLASSÉ EN **1855** —

Owner: The Frey family

AREA UNDER VINE 110 hectares

PRODUCTION 150,000 bottles

SOIL Gravel

GRAPE VARIETIES 60% Cabernet Sauvignon, 30% Merlot, 10% Petit Verdot

AGEING 18 months - New barrels: 50%

SECOND WINE Moulin de La Lagune

33290 Ludon-Médoc
Tel.: +33 (0)5 57 88 82 77

Winemaker: Caroline Frey

contact@chateau-lalagune.com
www.chateau-lalagune.com

lalagunegrandcruclasse

chateaulalaguneofficiel

Château La Lagune is located on an alluvial terrace parallel to the palus (rich soil that is less good for winegrowing) bordering the river. The "Village de La Lagune" was founded here in 1525. Circa 1587, a tenant farm was built in its place and gradual investments led to the transformation of several modest leaseholds into a major winegrowing estate.

There have been several owners over the years. The lovely château we know today was built between 1730 and 1734. In 1855, La Lagune joined the select club of grands crus classés as a third growth. The Sèze family acquired La Lagune in 1886, and remained owners until 1956. They were followed by Georges Brunet, who gave a new impetus to the estate before selling it to the Ayala Champagne House in 1964.

The estate was handed over to the Frey family in 2000, who undertook large-scale investments to achieve overall excellence and respect for the environment. Château la Lagune has been certified organic since 2016.

Château de Lamarque

Owner: The Gromand d'Evry family

The seigneury of Lamarque takes its name from "la marche" (meaning "the marches") since it was located on the border of the province of Guyenne).

The current fortress was built one thousand years ago by Garsion de Lamarque, the ancestor of Pierre-Gilles Gromand d'Evry, to defend the Médoc against Vikings invading from the Gironde Estuary. It was also the site of fierce assaults by the English during the Hundred Years' War...

Thalésie de Lamarque, granddaughter of Garsion, owned the estate in 1247. She left her mark on the château and its surrounding vineyard, which is part of the soul of the estate.

Her spirit continues to accompany the talented men and women who are caretakers of this superb terroir, and who give the wines of Lamarque their brilliance, freshness, sensuality, and long aftertaste.

763 years later, Thalésie d'Everlange - the granddaughter of Marie-Hélène and Pierre-Gilles, embodies the same values.

AREA UNDER VINE 45 hectares

PRODUCTION 160,000 bottles

SOIL 85% Garonne gravel, 5% clay-gravel, 10% traces of ironpan

GRAPE VARIETIES 45% Cabernet Sauvignon, 45% Merlot, 10% Petit Verdot

AGEING 16 to 18 months - New barrels: 40%

SECOND WINE Donjon de Lamarque

33460 Lamarque
Tel.: +33 (0) 5 56 58 90 03

President and Manager: Pierre-Gilles Gromand d'Evry
Co-president and Co-manager: Marie-Hélène Gromand d'Evry

lamarque@chateaudelamarque.fr
www.chateaudelamarque.fr

 Chateaudelamarque
 chateaudelamarque
 CHDELAMARQUE
 u/5574213025
 ID: pgg1122

Château
La Tour Carnet

— GRAND CRU CLASSÉ EN **1855** —

Owner: Bernard Magrez

AREA UNDER VINE 178 hectares

PRODUCTION 450,000 bottles

SOIL Pyrenean and Günz gravel on a clay-limestone bedrock

GRAPE VARIETIES 59% Merlot, 37% Cabernet Sauvignon, 3% Petit Verdot, 1% Cabernet Franc

AGEING 12 months - New barrels: 33%

SECOND WINE Les Pensées de La Tour Carnet

Route de Beychevelle
33112 Saint Laurent-Médoc
Tel.: +33 (0)5 56 73 30 90

Director of Vineyards for the Bernard Magrez Group: Frédéric Chabaneau
Estate Manager: Alix Combes

latour@latour-carnet.com
www.bernard-magrez.com

 LaTourCarnet
 bernardmagrez
 bernardmagrez
 bernardmagrez

Dating back to the 12th century, La Tour Carnet is a genuine medieval castle with a moat. The oldest château in the Médoc, it owes its name to the famous equerry Carnet, who fought valiantly beside Lord Jean de Foy. Carnet's courage and devotion were such that he ended up inheriting the estate. Éléonore, the sister of Michel de Montaigne, was one of several illustrious owners during the 16th century.

Following in her footsteps, the current owner, Bernard Magrez, has expended an enormous amount of time and energy in renovating the estate. His efforts have concerned the vineyard, cellars, and château.

Meticulous care is taken during pruning, leaf thinning, and green harvesting to reduce yields in the interest of quality. The grapes are handpicked into small crates and sorted by hand before being transferred by gravity flow into wooden fermentation vats and then into barrel. These are just a few of the practices that contribute to the excellence of this estate, which is included in the 1855 classification.

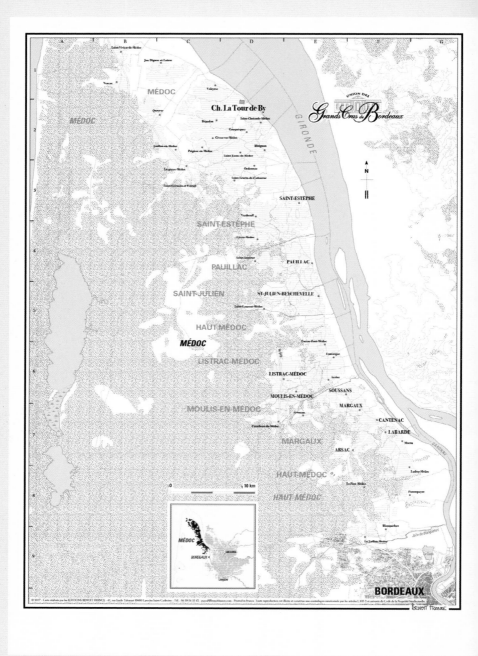

Ch. La Tour de By

CRU DE
MÉDOC

The Médoc is a huge triangular peninsula starting northwest of the city of Bordeaux, at a stream called the Jalle de Blanquefort, and going as far north as the Pointe de Grave. It is bordered by the Atlantic Ocean on the west and the Gironde Estuary on the east. Located off the northern tip of this peninsula, Cordouan, "the King of Lighthouses", reflects the long history of the Bordeaux wine trade and the necessity for merchant ships to have safe access up and down the Gironde Estuary.

Wine from the Médoc appellation comes mainly from vineyards located in the northern part of the peninsula, bordering the estuary, on a strip of land two to five km. wide, and 20 km. long, starting from Ordonnac in the south and going as far north as Vensac. The western boundary is limited at the drainage divide by a pine forest which serves as a natural windbreak against ocean gales.

Château
La Tour de By

Owners: Frédéric Le Clerc – Benjamin Richer de Forges

AREA UNDER VINE 80 hectares

PRODUCTION 450,000 bottles

SOIL Gravel on a iron hardpan subsoil

GRAPE VARIETIES 60% Cabernet Sauvignon, 35% Merlot, 5% Petit Verdot

AGEING 12 months - New barrels: 25%

SECOND WINE Château Cailloux de By

5 rue de La Tour de By - 33340 Bégadan
Tel.: +33(0)5 56 41 50 03

Manager: Frédéric Le Clerc
Sales Director: Benjamin Richer de Forges

info@latourdeby.fr
www.latourdeby.com

Château La Tour de By
@chateaulatourdeby

Vines have been grown at La Tour de By since the 16th century and records show that the château was acquired by Pierre Tizon, lord of the fiefdom of By, in 1599. The tower symbolising the estate is a former lighthouse built in the middle of the vines in 1825 to guide sailors navigating on the Gironde Estuary on foggy nights.

In 1965, Marc Pagès, an agricultural engineer from Tunisia, purchased this beautiful estate in the northern Médoc and was responsible for its restoration. He was assisted by Professor Émile Peynaud, whose advice contributed enormously to making the most of the remarkable terroir. Marc brought this Médoc estate up to its full potential during the four decades during which he managed it.

In 2005, his grandson, Frédéric Le Clerc followed his grandfather's winemaking philosophy combining quality, precision winemaking, and respect for traditional techniques.

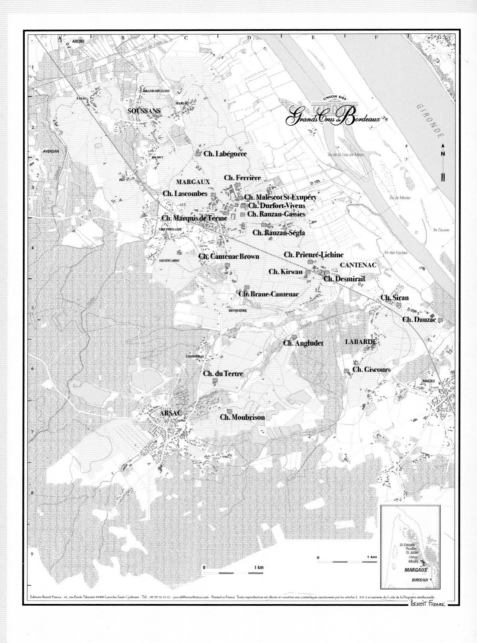

CRUS DE
MARGAUX

The name Margaux is magical and reflects a history of winemaking going back a thousand years. As with most vineyard close to the city of Bordeaux, wine production began during the Gallo-Roman period.

Records from the early 18th century refer to numerous winegrowing estates. While the château, whose name is eponymous with the appellation, already had a long history of selling wine, it was only in the late 18th century that other vineyard owners became aware of the value of their land and introduced the production and ageing methods that gave rise to the grands crus of Margaux.

It took more than a century after the famous 1855 classification for this large, complex region to put conflicts between communes behind it and for the rigorously delimited Margaux appellation to be recognised.

MARGAUX

Château Angludet

Owner: The Sichel family

AREA UNDER VINE 30 hectares

PRODUCTION 90,000 bottles

SOIL Gravel

GRAPE VARIETIES 46% Cabernet Sauvignon, 41% Merlot, 13% Petit Verdot

AGEING 12 months - New barrels: 35%

SECOND WINE Réserve d'Angludet

Château Angludet - 33460 Margaux-Cantenac
Tel.: +33 (0)5 57 88 71 41

Manager: Benjamin Sichel

contact@chateau-angludet.fr
www.chateau-angludet.fr

[f] **Chateau Angludet**
[◎] **chateauangludet**

Château Angludet belongs to the Sichel family, who worked as Bordeaux wine merchants for six generations. It is one of the oldest estates in the Médoc.

Records going back to the year 1150 mention a "noble residence" in Angludet, mean "Angle of High Land". The first lord of the manor, referred to in a deed dated 1273, was the knight Bertrand d'Angludet. The vineyard has had practically the same configuration since 1758 – over 250 years – which is exceedingly rare.

Diana and Peter Sichel fell in love with Angludet, which they acquired in 1961. Alongside Peter Sichel, they undertook a major renovation of the estate over a period of 40 years, establishing Angludet as one of the finest wines in Margaux. Since 1989, Benjamin Sichel manages the estate and oversees all aspects of viticulture and winemaking. He is also attentive to using natural, sustainable practices in the vineyard.

Château Brane-Cantenac

— GRAND CRU CLASSÉ EN 1855 —

Owner: Henri Lurton

Over three hundred years, the outstanding terroir of Château Brane-Cantenac has gained a legendary reputation.

In the 19th century, Baron Hector de Brane, nicknamed "Napoleon of the vines", developed the terroir and Château Brane-Cantenac become known as "the first of the second growths".

The wines of this château express their terroir composed of 72 hectares in the Margaux appellation. The vines are grown on deep gravel soil on the illustrious Brane plateau, where they benefit from excellent natural drainage. This plateau, known as "the heart of Brane", produces complex, brilliant, and classy wines.

Henri Lurton represents the fourth generation to follow in his ancestor's footsteps. Keen on innovation and the latest technology, Henri nevertheless remains faithful to the family's traditional values which form the intrinsic identity of Brane-Cantenac. Today, he continues to produce classy wines of outstanding quality.

AREA UNDER VINE 72 hectares

PRODUCTION 150,000 bottles

SOIL Deep gravel terraces from the Quaternary and Tertiary periods

GRAPE VARIETIES 55% Cabernet Sauvignon, 40% Merlot, 4% Cabernet Franc, 0.5% Petit Verdot, 0.5% Carmenère

AGEING 18 months - New barrels: 70%

SECOND WINE Baron de Brane

Chemin de Benqueyre
33460 Margaux-Cantenac
Tel.: +33 (0)5 57 88 83 33

Estate Manager: Christophe Capdeville
Marketing and Sales Director: Marie-Hélène Dussech

contact@brane-cantenac.com
www.brane-cantenac.com

 @branecantenac.chateau
 chateau_branecantenac
 @BRANE_CANTENAC

Château
Cantenac Brown

— GRAND CRU CLASSÉ EN 1855 —

Owner: The Simon Halabi family

AREA UNDER VINE 48 hectares

PRODUCTION 130,000 bottles

SOIL Garonne gravel

GRAPE VARIETIES 65% Cabernet Sauvignon, 30% Merlot, 5% Cabernet Franc

AGEING 16 months in barrel - New barrels: 60%

SECOND WINE BriO de Cantenac Brown

Château Cantenac Brown - 33460 Margaux
Tel.: +33 (0)5 57 88 81 81

General Director and Winemaker: José Sanfins

contact@cantenacbrown.com
www.cantenacbrown.com

Château Cantenac Brown
chateau_cantenac_brown
@Cantenac_Brown

John-Lewis Brown acquired this estate in the early 19th century and decided to build a Tudor-style château there reminiscent of his Scottish origins. This building, one of the most unusual in the Médoc, is surrounded by remarkable English-style grounds. A famous animal painter and lover of fine wine, Brown organised sumptuous receptions there until 1843, when the estate was sold to Monsieur Gromard.

The quality of the wine was acknowledged in the 1855 classification, when Cantenac-Brown was included among the third growths.

One hundred and fifty years later, the Simon Halabi family have given a new impetus to this estate, which they are determined to raise to the very highest level. José Sanfins presently manages Château Cantenac-Brown. He does his utmost to make the most of the magnificent terroir, lavishing the greatest of respect for the environment. This meticulous attention to detail continues into the cellar, where everything possible is done to produce an outstanding wine.

Château Dauzac

— GRAND CRU CLASSÉ EN **1855** —

Owner: S.A. Château Dauzac

Château Dauzac is a Margaux great growth in the 1855 classification, owned by the MAIF group and managed by Laurent Fortin since 2013. The estate has 49 hectares of vines in a single block, ideally located close to the Gironde Estuary and surrounded by forests and meadows. The vineyard's microclimate and unique gravel terroir are conducive to precision winegrowing on a plot-by-plot basis.

Château Dauzac continues to promote its status as a pioneer of technological and agricultural progress, and has experimented with several innovative practices (bouillie bordelaise, temperature-control, oak vats with two transparent staves, etc.). This Margaux estate is one of the most invested in biodiversity, producing wines that truly reflect their terroir.

Château Dauzac presents all the characteristics of a wine with excellent ageing potential, while Aurore de Dauzac offers instant pleasure.

AREA UNDER VINE 49 hectares

PRODUCTION 120,000 bottles

SOIL Deep gravel on a clay-gravel subsoil

GRAPE VARIETIES 68% Cabernet Sauvignon, 32% Merlot

AGEING 14 to 16 months - New barrels: 65 - 68%

SECOND WINE Aurore de Dauzac

———•———

Avenue Georges Johnston - 33460 Labarde
Tel.: +33 (0)5 57 88 32 10

Managing Director: Laurent Fortin

Contact@ChateauDauzac.com
www.ChateauDauzac.com

📘 @ChateauDauzac
📷 @ChateauDauzac
🐦 @dauzacchateau
💬 laurentfortin

Château
Desmirail

— GRAND CRU CLASSÉ EN **1855** —

Owner: Denis Lurton

AREA UNDER VINE 37 hectares

PRODUCTION 100,000 bottles

SOIL Deep gravel from the Quaternary period

GRAPE VARIETIES 60% Cabernet Sauvignon, 37% Merlot, 3% Petit Verdot

AGEING 12 months - New barrels: 50%

SECOND WINE Initial de Desmirail

28, avenue de la Ve République
33460 Margaux-Cantenac
Tel.: +33 (0)5 57 88 34 33

contact@desmirail.com
www.desmirail.com

 Chateaudesmirail
 @chateaudesmirail

Château Desmirail, included among the third growths in the 1855 classification, has an outstanding terroir bordering on the famous Route des Châteaux. The elegant 17th century manor house is located behind a majestic gate made of pink marble. The cellar features a vat room typical of those from the late 19th century Médoc.

Visitors can admire the magnificent roof structure and new wooden vats first used in the 2010 vintage.

Jean Desmirail gave his name to the château after marrying an heiress from the Rausan family in the late 17th century.

The current owner and manager, Denis Lurton, took over from his father, Lucien, in 1992. He has invested in modernising the estate on a regular basis ever since. Château Desmirail produces smooth, elegant wines in the classic Margaux style.

Château
Durfort-Vivens

— GRAND CRU CLASSÉ EN **1855** —

Owner: Gonzague Lurton

Founded in the 14th century by the Durfort de Duras family, the estate named Durfort-Vivens, was acclaimed by Thomas Jefferson and already at its peak in the late 18th century. The 1855 classification confirmed the reputation of the château, ranked among the Second Great Growths. In 1961, the estate was one of the first acquired by Lucien Lurton, as he embarked on his journey to find the greatest Bordeaux terroirs. His son Gonzague took over the vineyard in 1992 and, like his father, he made it his mission to develop a wine that expressed its full potential. His quest to produce well-balanced, characterful wines, while respecting nature and wildlife (vivens means "living" in Latin) led him to convert to biodynamic viticulture in 2009. In 2016, Durfort-Vivens became the first great growth estate in the 1855 classification to become Demeter-certified.

AREA UNDER VINE 55 hectares

PRODUCTION 250,000 bottles

SOIL Deep gravel from the Quaternary period with a sandy to sandy-clay matrix

GRAPE VARIETIES 80% Cabernet Sauvignon, 17% Merlot, 3% Cabernet Franc

AGEING 18 months on average - New barrels: 60% new French oak barrels

SECOND WINE Vivens

3 rue du Général de Gaulle - 33460 Margaux
Tel.: +33 (0)5 57 88 31 02

Manager: Gonzague Lurton
Technical Director: Léopold Valentin

infos@durfort-vivens.com
www.durfort-vivens.com

@Durfort.vivens
chateau_durfort_vivens
ChateauDurfortVivens

Château
Ferrière

— GRAND CRU CLASSÉ EN 1855 —

Owner: Claire Villars Lurton

AREA UNDER VINE 22 hectares

PRODUCTION 70,000 bottles

SOIL Deep gravel on marl limestone subsoil

GRAPE VARIETIES 60% Cabernet Sauvignon, 35% Merlot, 4% Petit Verdot , 1% Cabernet Franc

AGEING 18 months - New barrels: 40%

SECOND WINE Les Remparts de Ferrière

33 bis rue de la Trémoille - 33460 Margaux
Tel.: +33 (0)5 57 88 76 65

Production Manager: Gérard Fenouillet

infos@ferriere.com
www.ferriere.com

 @chateau.ferriere.margaux
 @chateau_ferriere
 @chateauferriere

Located in the heart of Margaux, Château Ferrière was founded in the 18th century by Gabriel Ferrière, a shipbroker and royal huntsman. The small size of the vineyard and its beautiful terroir result in a rare, highly-prized wine, ranked as a third great growth in the 1855 classification.

The estate belonged to the same family for nearly 300 years, before Bernadette Merlaut-Villars acquired it in 1988. The current owner, Claire Villars Lurton, undertook renovation work at the Château Ferrière in 2013, including converting the estate to organic and biodynamic vineyard management to bring it into line with the highest standards. This estate's wines were certified organic in 2015 and biodynamic in 2018.

The decision to convert the vineyard is the result of a general awareness of the need to preserve the terroir's outstanding heritage, made possible thanks to sustainable viticulture.

Château Giscours

— GRAND CRU CLASSÉ EN 1855 —

The history of Château Giscours dates back to the 14th century. However, the true creation of the estate can be considered to date from the purchase of the "maison noble de Guyscoutz" by Pierre de L'homme, a rich cloth merchant, in 1552. The estate underwent a golden age in the 19th century thanks to wealthy and influential owners such as the Promis, Pescatore, and Cruse families. This is also when Giscours underwent a number of important changes: the château was transformed into a neoclassic palace, the grounds were landscaped by Eugène Bülher, rare tree species were planted, and immense outbuildings were built, including the famous Ferme Suzanne.

In 1995, Éric Albada Jelgersma took over management and set about meticulously renovating the vineyard and buildings to provide this prestigious estate with the status worthy of a great growth in the 1855 classification.

Today, Dennis, Derk and Valérie Albada Jelgersma have followed in their father's footsteps in their mission to produce great wines that fully express their magnificent terroir.

AREA UNDER VINE 100 hectares

PRODUCTION 280,000 bottles

SOIL Deep Garonne gravel

GRAPE VARIETIES 64% Cabernet Sauvignon, 30% Merlot, 3% Cabernet Franc, 3% Petit Verdot

AGEING 15 to 17 months - New barrels: 50%

SECOND WINE La Sirène de Giscours

---

10 route de Giscours - 33460 Labarde
Tel.: +33 (0)5 57 97 09 09

President: Dennis Albada Jelgersma
Managing Director: Alexander van Beek
Sales Director: Laure Bastard

giscours@chateau-giscours.fr
www.chateau-giscours.fr

Château Giscours

@chateaugiscours

@giscours_gcc

Château Kirwan

— GRAND CRU CLASSÉ EN 1855 —

Owner: Schröder & Schÿler and Cie

AREA UNDER VINE 37 hectares

PRODUCTION 100,000 bottles

SOIL Pyrenean gravel on the Cantenac plateau and sandy-gravel on a clay subsoil

GRAPE VARIETIES 47% Cabernet Sauvignon, 35% Merlot, 10% Cabernet Franc, 8% Petit Verdot

AGEING 18 to 21 months in French oak barrels - New barrels: 33%

SECOND WINE Charmes de Kirwan

33460 Cantenac
Tel.: + 33(0)5 57 87 64 55

Director of Sales Development and Communication: Sophie Schÿler-Thierry
Managing Director: Philippe Delfaut

mail@chateau-kirwan.com
www.chateau-kirwan.com

 Château Kirwan - Grand Cru Classé 1855

 chateaukirwan

 Chateau_Kirwan

 chateaukirwan

 chateaukirwan

Château Kirwan was built in the late 18th century by the illustrious Irish businessman Mark Kirwan. He combined two small neighbouring vineyards in the village of Cantenac and gave his name to the new entity.

The Godard family acquired Château Kirwan around 1870. They expanded the vineyards and designed beautiful grounds and gardens with a fish pond and rose arbour.

Accustomed to selling the estate's wine at their wine and spirits firm (Schröder & Schÿler), the Schÿler family, originally from the Hanseatic League and based in Bordeaux since 1739, purchased the estate in 1926.

In 2007, following major investments, family heirs Sophie, Nathalie and Yann Schÿler developed their wine expertise with support from the estate's managing director, the experienced oenologist Philippe Delfaut. They installed a new vat room in 2015 (featuring 37 cement vats shaped like a tulip) and large contemporary cellar to showcase the terroir and optimise precision winemaking methods.

Château Labégorce

Owner: The Perrodo family, represented by Nathalie Perrodo Samani

This elegant neoclassical estate is located on the famous Route des Châteaux. Seventy hectares of the 250-hectare estate are devoted to viticulture. Bordering on châteaux Margaux and Lascombes, this property is mentioned in the 1868 edition of Cocks and Feret's ("Bordeaux and its Wines"), which tells us of the existence of "a vineyard belonging to the Noble de la Bégorce family". The château is described as "one of the most beautiful and best situated in the commune of Margaux".

The Perrodo family purchased Labégorce in 1989 and set to work restoring the château building and vineyard. They also improved winemaking techniques, resulting in a charming, elegant wine with a beautiful tannic structure and fruity notes.

The Perrodo family also acquired Château Marquis d'Alesme, a third growth Margaux, in 2006, which they aim to transform into one of the most prestigious wines in the appellation.

AREA UNDER VINE 70 hectares

PRODUCTION 120,000 to 140,000 bottles

SOIL 70% sand and gravel, 30% sand and limestone

GRAPE VARIETIES 50% Cabernet Sauvignon, 45% Merlot, 3% Cabernet Franc, 2% Petit Verdot

AGEING 12 to 14 months - New barrels: 40 - 50%

SECOND WINE Zédé de Labégorce

1 route de Labégorce - 33460 Margaux
Tel.: +33 (0)5 57 88 71 32

Managing Director: Marjolaine Maurice de Coninck
Sales Director: Delphine Dariol Kolasa

contact@labegorce.com
www.chateau-labegorce.com

Equipe Labegorce

Château Lascombes

Owner: MACSF
(Mutuelle d'Assurances du Corps de Santé Français)

AREA UNDER VINE 130 hectares

PRODUCTION 300,000 bottles

SOIL Clay-limestone, clay-gravel and gravel

GRAPE VARIETIES 50% Merlot, 45% Cabernet Sauvignon, 5% Petit Verdot

AGEING 18 months for the first wine (Château Lascombes), 16 months for the second wine (Chevalier de Lascombes) - New barrels: 70 - 80% new barrels for the first wine

SECOND WINE Chevalier de Lascombes

1 Cours de Verdun - 33460 Margaux
Tel.: +33 (0)5 57 88 70 66

Managing Director of the MACSF group: Stéphane Dessirier
Managing Director of Château Lascombes: Dominique Befve

contact@chateau-lascombes.fr
www.chateau-lascombes.com/

Château Lascombes
chateau_lascombes
Château Lascombes

Château Lascombes is a second growth in the 1855 classification. The estate's 130 hectares of vines are grown on a wide variety of clay-limestone, clay-gravel, and gravelly soils. 120 hectares are located in the Margaux appellation and 10 are in the Haut-Médoc. The vineyard is characterised by its high percentage of Merlot grapes, made up of 50% Merlot, 45% Cabernet Sauvignon and 5% Petit Verdot.

The MACSF (Mutuelle d'Assurances du Corps de Santé Francais) has owned Château Lascombes since 2011, and produces high-quality wines that respect traditional Médoc techniques alongside Dominique Befve (Managing Director since 2001) and Michel Rolland (consulting oenologist).

The estate produces a second wine, Chevalier de Lascombes, renowned for its elegance, beautiful concentration, and great finesse.

Château Malescot Saint-Exupéry

— GRAND CRU CLASSÉ EN 1855 —

Owner: Jean-Luc Zuger

Château Malescot St-Exupéry owes its name to two former owners: Simon Malescot, a royal councillor to the Bordeaux parliament, who acquired the estate in 1697, and Count Jean-Baptiste de Saint-Exupéry, who owned it from 1827 to 1853.

Paul Zuger and his son Roger purchased the château, located in the middle of the town of Margaux, in June 1955. After more than thirty years of unstinting efforts, Malescot St-Exupéry's coat of arms has never been truer: Semper Ad Altum (or "always higher"). The 45-hectare estate has 28 hectares of vines on a fine terroir that "overlooks the river" - indicative of the best vineyard sites according to an old local saying.

Connoisseurs greatly appreciate the outstanding bouquet of this great growth, whose fruitiness and body go together beautifully with meat dishes and cheeses.

AREA UNDER VINE 28 hectares

PRODUCTION 120,000 bottles

SOIL Pyrenean gravel

GRAPE VARIETIES 50% Cabernet Sauvignon, 35% Merlot, 10% Cabernet Franc, 5% Petit Verdot

AGEING 13 to 15 months in barrel

SECOND WINE La Dame de Malescot

16, rue Georges Mandel - 33460 Margaux
Tel.: +33 (0)5 57 88 97 20

Manager: Jean-Luc Zuger
Technical Director: Gilles Pouget

malescotstexupery@malescot.com
www.malescot.com

Château
Marquis de Terme

— **GRAND CRU CLASSÉ EN 1855** —

Owner: The Sénéclauze family

AREA UNDER VINE 39 hectares

PRODUCTION 130,000 bottles

SOIL Gravel with quartz and quartzite.
Pockets of soil with a greater concentration
of clay deep down

GRAPE VARIETIES 60% Cabernet Sauvignon,
35% Merlot, 5% Petit Verdot

AGEING 18 months in French oak barrels -
New barrels: 50%

SECOND WINE La Couronne de Marquis de
Terme

3 route de Rauzan- 33460 Margaux
Tel.: + 33 (0) 5 57 88 30 01

Managing Director: Ludovic David

mdt@chateau-marquis-de-terme.com
www.chateau-marquis-de-terme.com

Château Marquis de Terme, Grand Cru
Classé, Margaux

chateaumarquisdeterme

@MarquisDeTerme

In 1762, the Marquis de Terme gave his name to the wine estate that was part of his wife's dowry.

In 1787 Thomas Jefferson, future president of the United States, put this wine on the map, ranking it as one of his favourites. In 1855, the estate joined the exclusive club of Grand Cru Classés. The Sénéclauze family acquired the château in 1935 and continued to develop it generation after generation. In 2009, Ludovic David was appointed Managing Director, and implemented various technical and viticultural innovations, including plot-by-plot vineyard management, environmentally friendly winegrowing practices and "vinification intégrale" barrel fermentation to enable the terroir to fully express itself and produce well-balanced wines. Since then, the château has opened its doors for visitors to share their love of fine wine via wine tours and made-to-measure workshops. Today, Château Marquis de Terme has established its revival as an estate at the crossroads between tradition and innovation.

Château Monbrison

GRAND VIN
DE
Margaux

Owner: Laurent Vonderheyden

Château Monbrison is a family estate ideally located in the heart of the Margaux appellation and has been owned by the Davis-Vonderheyden family for nearly a century.

It benefits from an outstanding location, nestled at the end of a beautiful path lined with umbrella pines, in a century-old old park.

Situated on the highest plateaux in the Margaux appellation, the estate is surrounded on all sides by 15.5 hectares of vines, rooted in fine, deep gravel.

The estate's philosophy revolves around its ongoing quest to preserve the intrinsic characteristics of the terroir.

The golden rule lies in combining tradition and modernity. Monbrison wines are quintessentially aromatic, fruity, and elegant.

Its world-famous reputation continues to attract new, loyal consumers. Since January 2018, Laurent Vonderheyden and his youngest daughter, Alix, manage Château Monbrison, working together to shape its destiny.

AREA UNDER VINE 15.5 hectares

PRODUCTION 48,000 bottles

SOIL Pyrenean gravel

GRAPE VARIETIES 70% Cabernet Sauvignon, 20% Merlot, 7% Cabernet Franc, 3% Petit Verdot

AGEING 18 months in French oak barrels - New barrels: 40%

SECOND WINE Bouquet de Monbrison

1, Allée de Monbrison - 33460 Arsac
Tel.: +33 (0)5 56 58 80 04

Technical Director: Marc Daulouède

monbrison@hotmail.fr
www.chateaumonbrison.com

 Chateau Monbrison Margaux
 Chateau Monbrison Margaux

Château Prieuré-Lichine

— **GRAND CRU CLASSÉ EN 1855** —

Owner: Groupe Ballande

AREA UNDER VINE 78 hectares

PRODUCTION 192,000 bottles

SOIL Pyrenean and Günz gravel

GRAPE VARIETIES 55% Cabernet Sauvignon, 40% Merlot, 5% Petit Verdot

AGEING 14 to 16 months - New barrels: 40%

SECOND WINE Confidences de Prieuré Lichine

———•———

34 avenue de la Vᵉ république
33460 Cantenac
Tel.: +33 (0)5 57 88 36 28

Technical Director: Étienne Charrier
Sales and Communication Director: Lise Latrille

contact@prieure-lichine.fr
www.prieure-lichine.fr

@Château Prieuré-Lichine
@chateau.prieurelichine
@PrieureLichine

Founded in the 12th century by monks from Vertheuil Abbey, the prieuré (or "priory") of Cantenac has produced well-reputed wines from the very beginning.

In 1951, Alexis Lichine, nicknamed "the Pope of Wine", took over the estate and added his name two years later. Thanks to his patient determination, he was able to add new vineyard plots, modernise the cellars, and renovate the monks' former living quarters. Château Prieuré-Lichine's fate was linked to that of the Lichine family for half a century.

Now owned by the Ballande group, the château has entered a dynamic new phase of its history, thanks to the purchase of 8 additional hectares in 2012 and the installation of a new vat.

A new approach to managing far-flung vineyard plots has turned this diversity into a decided advantage, enabling Prieuré-Lichine to express the full complexity of its terroir thanks to an experienced and devoted winemaking team.

Château Rauzan-Gassies

— **GRAND CRU CLASSÉ EN 1855** —

Owner: The Quié family

Château Rauzan-Gassies is a second growth in the 1855 classification, located in the Margaux appellation. It owes its name to Chevalier de Rauzan, who transformed the "Maison Noble de Gassies" into a famous wine estate in the 17th century.

Monsieur Paul Quié was greatly attracted to the château's outstanding terroir and acquired the estate in 1946. Continuing in the family tradition, Quié's son, Jean-Michel, now manages the estate alongside his children.

Château Rauzan-Gassies produces deeply-coloured, elegant, and complex wines with a velvety texture and excellent ageing potential. The Quié family is passionate about making fine wine and delighted to offer special moments to share with family and friends.

AREA UNDER VINE 28 hectares
PRODUCTION 70,000 bottles
SOIL Deep gravel, gravelly sand
GRAPE VARIETIES 55% Cabernet Sauvignon, 43% Merlot, 2% Petit Verdot
AGEING 18 months including 12 to 14 months in barrel - New barrels: 50 - 55%
SECOND WINE Gassies

1, rue Alexis Millardet
33460 Margaux
Tel.: +33 (0) 5 57 88 71 88
rauzangassies@domaines-quie.com
www.rauzangassies.fr

Château Rauzan-Ségla

— GRAND CRU CLASSÉ EN 1855 —

Owner: CHANEL

AREA UNDER VINE 70 hectares

SOIL Clay gravel on a Quaternary terrace Patchwork of deep, fine gravel

GRAPE VARIETIES 62% Cabernet Sauvignon, 36% Merlot, 1% Petit Verdot, 1% Cabernet Franc

AGEING 18 months - New barrels: 60%

SECOND WINE Ségla

Rue Alexis Millardet - 33460 Margaux
Tel.: +33 (0)5 57 88 82 10

Managing Director: Nicolas Audebert
Export Managers: Jean-Basile Roland and Andréane Gomard

contact@rauzansegla.com
www.chateaurauzansegla.com

 chateaurauzanseglaofficial
 chateaurauzansegla

Located just outside the village of Margaux, the 70-hectare vineyards of Château Rauzan-Ségla are considered a priceless treasure, reflecting the diversity of soils in the appellation. Benefiting from good drainage, the estate's alluvial gravel soils are conducive to deep rooting, enabling the beauty of the terroir and grape varieties to be expressed to the full.

These great terroirs, lovingly tended to for over 350 years, were praised by the visionary Pierre de Rauzan and listed in the 1855 classification.

They have belonged to CHANEL since 1994 and wonderfully reflect the estate's philosophy of excellence, based on the joint efforts and dedication of our teams to producing intensely elegant wines.

MARGAUX

Château Siran

Owner: The Miailhe family

Château Siran has 25 hectares of vines in the Margaux appellation and has been owned by the Miailhe family for 160 years. Perched on a plateau of fine siliceous gravel with good sun exposure close to the river, it is unquestionably one of the jewels of the Margaux appellation.

This 88-hectare wine estate benefits from a favourable ecosystem featuring woods, streams, parkland, ponds, an orchard, and prairies close to the vineyard. Conscious of its ecological responsibilities, the team at Siran have practised sustainable agriculture since 2000 and began experimenting with organic agriculture in several plots in 2018.

Siran wines are refined, elegant, and express their terroir, while reflecting the search for a perfect balance between tannin, fruit and acidity. The wines are profound, subtle, charming and complex, becoming more refined over time. Siran's excellent ageing potential is characteristic of the Margaux great growths.

AREA UNDER VINE 25 hectares

PRODUCTION 80,000 to 100,000 bottles

SOIL Alluvial plateau covered by a fine siliceous gravel topsoil

GRAPE VARIETIES 46% Merlot, 44% Cabernet Sauvignon, 9% Petit Verdot, 1% Cabernet Franc

AGEING 12 to 18 months -
New barrels: 35 - 40%

SECOND WINE S de Siran

13 avenue du comte J-B de Lynch
33460 Labarde
Tel.: +33 (0)5 57 88 34 04

Co-managers: Édouard and Brigitte Miailhe

info@chateausiran.com
www.chateausiran.com

f @ChateauSiran
@ @ChateauSiran
@ChateauSiran

Château du Tertre

— GRAND CRU CLASSÉ EN 1855 —

Owner: The Albada Jelgersma family

AREA UNDER VINE 52 hectares

PRODUCTION 120,000 bottles

SOIL Günz gravel and sand

GRAPE VARIETIES 50% Cabernet Sauvignon, 23% Merlot, 14% Cabernet Franc, 13% Petit Verdot

AGEING 15 to 17 months - New barrels: 45%

SECOND WINE Les Hauts du Tertre

14 Allée du Tertre - 33460 Arsac
Tel.: +33 (0)5 57 88 52 52

Managing Director: Alexander van Beek
Sales director: Laure Bastard

tertre@chateaudutertre.fr
www.chateaudutertre.fr

Château du Tertre
@chateaudutertre
@tertre_gcc

Located on one of the highest and most beautiful gravelly rises in the Margaux appellation, Château du Tertre was created in the 18th century by an important Irish merchant, Pierre Mitchell, who fell in love with the Bordeaux region and its wines. The founder of the first glassworks in Bordeaux, this refined, innovative man realised one of his fondest dreams by establishing his own fine wine estate. Other famous families followed in his footsteps, including the Koenigswarters and rich bankers close to Emperor Napoleon III. The quality of the wine was such that it was included among the Margaux great growths in the 1855 classification.

In 1997, Éric Albada Jelgersma acquired the estate. Thanks to major investments, Château du Tertre now expresses its intrinsically elegant personality. Today, Dennis, Derk and Valérie Albada Jelgersma continue the family tradition, ensuring the future of this outstanding estate.

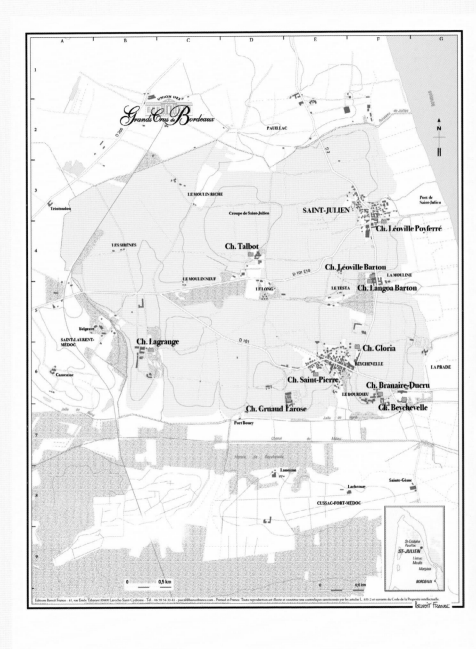

UNION DES
Grands Crus de Bordeaux

PAUILLAC

LE MOULIN RICHE

Trintaudon

Croupe de Saint-Julien

SAINT-JULIEN

Port de
Saint-Julien

LES SIRÈNES

Ch. Talbot

Ch. Léoville Poyferré

D 101 E10

Ch. Léoville Barton

LA MOULINE

LE MOULIN NEUF

LE LONG

LE TESTA

Ch. Langoa Barton

Belgrave

SAINT-LAURENT-
MÉDOC

Ch. Lagrange

D 101

Ch. Gloria

BEYCHEVELLE

LA PRADE

Camensac

Ch. Saint-Pierre

Ch. Branaire-Ducru

LE BOURDIEU

Port Bouey

Ch. Gruaud Larose

Jalle du Nord

Ch. Beychevelle

Chenal du Milieu

Marais de Beychevelle

Lansac

Lachenay

Sainte-Gême

CUSSAC-FORT-MÉDOC

0   0,5 km

St-Estèphe
Pauillac
ST-JULIEN
Listrac
Moulis
Margaux

BORDEAUX

0   0,8 km

Éditions Benoît France - 41, rue Emile Tabarant 89400 Laroche-Saint-Cydroine - Tél . 03 59 54 35 42 - pascal@benoitfrance.com . Printed in France. Toute reproduction est illicite et constitue une contrefaçon sanctionnée par les articles L. 335-2 et suivants du Code de la Propriété intellectuelle.

BENOÎT FRANCE

CRUS DE
SAINT-JULIEN

The parish of Saint-Julien dates back to the 7th century. Originally named Saint-Julien-de-Reignac, the town became known as Saint-Julien-Beychevelle in the early 20th century, combining the name of the small port and that of the hamlet famous for its fine wines.

Starting in the 17th century, aristocrats and other land owners made the most of the winegrowing potential of their outstanding terroir. They were responsible for creating the great estates included in the 1855 classification.

SAINT-JULIEN

CHÂTEAU BEYCHEVELLE

— SAINT-JULIEN —

Château Beychevelle

— GRAND CRU CLASSÉ EN 1855 —

Owner: Grands Millésimes de France

AREA UNDER VINE 92.5 hectares

PRODUCTION 240,000 to 260,000 bottles

SOIL Deep Garonne gravel

GRAPE VARIETIES 56% Cabernet Sauvignon, 40% Merlot, 1% Cabernet Franc, 3% Petit Verdot

AGEING 18 months - New barrels: 60%

SECOND WINE Amiral de Beychevelle

Château Beychevelle
33250 Saint-Julien-Beychevelle
Tel.: +33 (0)5 56 73 20 70

Manager: Nobuhiro Tori
Director: Philippe Blanc

beychevelle@beychevelle.com
www.beychevelle.com

ChateauBeychevelle1855

Beychevelle1855

Beychevelle1855

The spirit of Château Beychevelle was forged over three centuries.

During the reign of Henri III, the estate was the fief of the Dukes of Épernon, including the first of that name, Jean-Louis Nogaret de La Valette, an admiral in the French navy. Derived from the Old French "Baisse-Voile", meaning "lowered sails", Beychevelle takes its name from a legend that tells how ships passing in front of his estate lowered their sails as a sign of allegiance to this powerful man. This is reflected in the château's emblem, which depicts a ship with a griffin (the guardian of Dionysus' wines in Greek mythology) on the prow.

Built in the 17th century and reconstructed by Marquis de Brassier in 1757, the château was restored to its original splendour in the late 20th century.

The elegance of Beychevelle's architecture is reflected in its refined, well-balanced wine served at prestigious tables around the world.

The estate's owners are also very respectful of the environment and the estate has obtained integrated vineyard management certification.

SAINT-JULIEN

Château
Branaire-Ducru

— GRAND CRU CLASSÉ EN 1855 —

Owner: The Maroteaux family

The first person to own the estate in 1680, Jean-Baptiste Braneyre, was well aware of the superb winegrowing potential of its gravelly soil located a stone's throw from the Gironde Estuary. The 1855 classification was later to confirm the quality of the terroir.

In 1988, the family group asked Patrick Maroteaux, to write a new page in the history of this great growth. He consequently set out to make quality an absolute priority and do everything possible to express Branaire-Ducru's intrinsic personality and complexity. Consisting primarily of Cabernet Sauvignon, the estate's wines are characterised by their pure, fruity aromas and freshness. Branaire-Ducru is invariably elegant and a quintessential Saint-Julien in every vintage.

As the representative of the second generation, every effort is made to ensure all our great bottles evoke discovery, pleasure, and emotion for wine enthusiasts around the world.

AREA UNDER VINE 60 hectares

PRODUCTION Approximately 180,000 bottles

SOIL Deep gravel from the Quaternary Period on a clay subsoil

GRAPE VARIETIES 65% Cabernet Sauvignon, 28% Merlot, 4% Petit Verdot, 3% Cabernet Franc

AGEING 18 months - New barrels: 60%

SECOND WINE Duluc de Branaire-Ducru

1 Chemin du Bourdieu - 33250 Saint-Julien
Tel.: +33 (0)5 56 59 25 86

President/co-owner: François-Xavier Maroteaux
Director: Jean-Dominique Videau

branaire@branaire.com
www.branaire.com

f @châteauBranaireDucru
◎ @chateaubranaireducru
▾ @fxmaroteaux

Château Gloria

Owner: The Triaud family

AREA UNDER VINE 50 hectares

SOIL Günz gravel on a sandy-clay subsoil

GRAPE VARIETIES 65% Cabernet Sauvignon, 25% Merlot, 5% Cabernet Franc, 5% Petit Verdot

AGEING in barrels for 14 months - New barrels: 40%

SECOND WINE Château Peymartin

Château Gloria
33250 Saint-Julien Beychevelle
Tel.: +33 (0)5 56 59 08 18

Co-managers: Jean Triaud and Vanessa Triaud-Amougou

contact@domaines-martin.com
www.domaines-henri-martin.com

ChateauSaintPierre/

Designed by Henri Martin, this estate is one-of-a-kind. The 50-hectare vineyard has expanded over the years, with the gradual addition of plots exclusively from the great growths in the 1855 classification.

The outstanding terroir and meticulous care taken in the vineyard and cellar have helped produce world-famous wines.

Château Gruaud Larose

— **GRAND CRU CLASSÉ EN 1855** —

Owner: Jean Merlaut

The abbot Father Gruaud founded Château Gruaud Larose in 1725, which he left to his nephew, Chevalier de Larose in1781, who the estate is now named after.

Gruaud Larose has belonged to the Merlaut family since 1997. They were responsible for introducing sustainable development and organic methods in the vineyard, with great respect for the terroir.

Featuring a single block of vines grown on a rise consisting of deep Garonne gravel from the Quaternary period (about 600,000 years old), Château Gruaud Larose is one of the most historic estates in the Médoc which fully deserves its second growth rank in the Saint-Julien classification.

As befits a wine whose motto is "The King of Wines and the Wine of Kings", Cabernet Sauvignon is the leading grape variety in this terroir, responsible for the excellent reputation of wines from this estate.

AREA UNDER VINE 82 hectares

PRODUCTION 140,000 bottles

SOIL Garonne gravel from the Quaternary period deposited over 600,000 years ago

GRAPE VARIETIES 61% Cabernet Sauvignon, 29% Merlot, 7% Cabernet Franc, 3% Petit Verdot

AGEING 18 to 24 months in new barrels (85%), the remainder are aged in barrels previously used for one vintage. 100% French oak barrels

SECOND WINE Sarget de Gruaud

Château Gruaud-Larose
33250 Saint-Julien Beychevelle
Tel.: + 33 (0) 5 56 73 15 20

Managing Director: Nicolas Sinoquet
Sales Director: Arnaud Frédéric

gl@gruaud-larose.com
www.gruaud-larose.com

Château Gruaud Larose
Château Gruaud Larose

Château Lagrange

— **GRAND CRU CLASSÉ EN 1855** —

Owner: Suntory

AREA UNDER VINE 118 hectares

PRODUCTION 300,000 bottles

SOIL Two Günz gravel rises

GRAPE VARIETIES 68% Cabernet Sauvignon, 27% Merlot, 5% Petit Verdot

AGEING 18 to 20 months - New barrels: 60%

SECOND WINE Les Fiefs de Lagrange

33250 Saint-Julien-Beychevelle
Tel.: +33 (0)5 56 73 38 38

Vice-President: Keiichi Shiina
Managing Director: Matthieu Bordes

contact@chateau-lagrange.com
www.chateau-lagrange.com

ChateauLagrange1855

chateaulagrange

LagrangeGCC

Matthieu BORDES
ID:wxid_8c0x9niwb4rz22

Château Lagrange's reputation as a winegrowing estate emerged in the 17th century. Lagrange was classified as a third growth in the 1855 classification thanks to the passion and hard work of Count Dûchatel, who owned the château from 1842 to 1874. The estate stretches over 280 hectares, 120 of which are dedicated to winegrowing.

In 1983, the Suntory group, a leading Japanese wine and spirits firm, acquired Lagrange and invested heavily in a spectacular renovation. Priority was given to the vineyard, followed by modernising the vat room and cellars. Efforts undertaken since the 1980s have helped produce powerful, elegant wines characteristic of great Saint-Julien wines.

Today, a new duo, Matthieu Bordes and Keiichi Shiina, continue to the quest for excellence, producing environmentally-friendly wines that limit the estate's carbon footprint.

Château Langoa Barton

— GRAND CRU CLASSÉ EN 1855 —

Owner: The Barton family

Château Langoa Barton was purchased by an Irishman, Hugh Barton, in 1821. He was undoubtedly attracted to the château's elegant architecture and magnificent façade dating back to 1758. The estate, which was classified a third growth in 1855, has always remained under family ownership.

Today, Anthony Barton's daughter, Lilian Barton Sartorius, manages the family estates. Her two children, Mélanie and Damien, represent the tenth generation of winegrowers, and are highly invested in managing the châteaux and promoting the family's wines.

The vines of Langoa Barton are grown in the southern part of the estate. This Saint-Julien great growth is delicious and charming, displaying expressive red fruit notes with a silky texture and well-balanced structure.

AREA UNDER VINE 20 hectares

PRODUCTION 80,000 bottles

SOIL Gravel on a clay subsoil

GRAPE VARIETIES 57% Cabernet Sauvignon, 34% Merlot, 9% Cabernet Franc

AGEING 18 months in French oak barrels - New barrels: 60%

SECOND WINE Lady Langoa

Route des Châteaux
33250 Saint Julien Beychevelle
Tel.: +33 (0)5 56 59 06 05

Brand Ambassador: Damien Barton Sartorius
President of the Supervisory Council: Anthony Barton

chateau@barton-family-wines.com
www.barton-family-wines.com

 @bartonwine
 @bartonwine
 @bartonwine

Château
Léoville Barton

— **GRAND CRU CLASSÉ EN 1855** —

Owner: The Barton family

AREA UNDER VINE 50 hectares

PRODUCTION 180,000 bottles

SOIL Gravel on a clay subsoil

GRAPE VARIETIES 74% Cabernet Sauvignon, 23% Merlot, 3% Cabernet Franc

AGEING 18 months in French oak barrels - New barrels: 60%

SECOND WINE La Réserve de Léoville Barton

Route des Châteaux
33250 Saint-Julien Beychevelle
Tel.: +33 (0)5 56 59 06 05

President: Lilian Barton Sartorius
General Director: Mélanie Barton Sartorius

chateau@barton-family-wines.com
www.barton-family-wines.com

f @bartonwine
◎ @bartonwine
🐦 @bartonwine

In 1826, Hugh Barton, owner of Château Langoa Barton, purchased part of the vineyards of the Léoville estate, which was then renamed "Léoville Barton". The quality of the estate's wines was acknowledged in the famous 1855 classification, when it was listed as a second growth. The estate is still owned by the Barton family who believe very much in the importance of the terroir. Together, they produce signature Saint-Julien wines with superb finesse, balance, and a long-lasting freshness.

Twice in the history of the Bartons, one of the family members has been forced to flee from France: in 1793 Hugh returned to Ireland during the French Revolution, and later, Ronald had to temporarily abandon the château in 1940. He returned in 1945 to produce a mythical vintage.

Today, Lilian Barton Sartorius represents the ninth generation of Bordeaux winegrowers and the oldest family to still own a great growth estate.

Château Léoville Poyferré

— GRAND CRU CLASSÉ EN 1855 —

Owner: The Cuvelier family

Located in the north of the prestigious Saint-Julien appellation, the vineyard covers different types of gravel soils, contributing to the balance, finesse and elegance of its wines.

Château Léoville Poyferré was born in 1840 following various divisions. The classification of 1855 endowed it with the rank of Second Grand Cru.

Wine merchant and owner of Château Le Crock (Cru Bourgeois in St Estèphe), the Cuvelier family acquired Châteaux Moulin Riche and Léoville Poyferre in 1920.

For 40 years, Didier Cuvelier carried out restructuring of the vineyard with respect for the soil and environment, with a recent focus on biodynamics. Innovative winemaking techniques are combined with traditional barrel ageing methods. After working together for a while, he passed the baton to his cousin Sara Lecompte Cuvelier in 2018.

The château continues reaching out to wine lovers around the world at home and at the estate.

AREA UNDER VINE 58 hectares
PRODUCTION 220,000 bottles
SOIL Garonne gravel
GRAPE VARIETIES 61% Cabernet Sauvignon, 27% Merlot, 8% Petit Verdot, 4% Cabernet Franc
AGEING 18 to 20 months - New barrels: 80%
SECOND WINE Pavillon de Léoville Poyferré

38 rue de Saint-Julien
33250 Saint-Julien Beychevelle
Tel.: + 33(0)5 56 59 08 30

Manager: Sara Lecompte Cuvelier
Oenologist: Isabelle Davin

lp@leoville-poyferre.fr
www.leoville-poyferre.fr

 château leoville poyferre
 chateau-leovillepoyferre

CHATEAU SAINT-PIERRE
SAINT-JULIEN

DOMAINES MARTIN

Château Saint-Pierre

— GRAND CRU CLASSÉ EN 1855 —

Owner: The Triaud family

AREA UNDER VINE 17 hectares

SOIL Günz gravel on a sandy-clay subsoil

GRAPE VARIETIES 75% Cabernet Sauvignon, 15% Merlot, 10% Cabernet Franc

AGEING 14 to 16 months in barrel - New barrels: 50%

SECOND WINE Esprit de Saint-Pierre

Adresse : Château Gloria
33250 Saint-Julien Beychevelle
Tel.: +33 (0)5 56 59 08 18

Co-managers: Jean Triaud and Vanessa Triaud Amougou

contact@domaines-martin.com
www.domaines-henri-martin.com

f ChateauSaintPierre

This 17th century Fourth Grand Cru Classé was gradually divided over several generations and inheritances. In 1982, by a stroke of luck and persistence, Henri Martin restored the vineyard to its former state in 1855 glory, which also marks the famous classification year.

Since then, and thanks to numerous investments, Saint-Pierre is universally recognised as the perfect representation of Grands Crus Classés in the prestigious Saint-Julien appellation.

Château Talbot

— GRAND CRU CLASSÉ EN 1855 —

Owner: The Bignon-cordier family

This imposing estate owes its name to Connétable Talbot, the English General and Governor of the province of Guyenne who was defeated at the famous Battle of Castillon in 1453.

In an ideal location bordering the Gironde Estuary, Talbot's vines are grown on some of the region's most prized gravelly rises renowned for producing great wines. Talbot is one of the oldest estates in the Médoc. It has been in the hands of experienced managers for centuries, and always shown to be worthy of its inclusion in the 1855 classification.

Owners of Talbot since 1918, the Cordier family have perpetuated their predecessors' commitment to quality. At Talbot, wine is very much past, present, and future, whereby traditional techniques are combined with technical innovations.

Thanks to an alliance between mankind and nature, as well as generations of experience, this outstanding terroir produces wines which vary depending on the vintage, but are always well-balanced and complex.

AREA UNDER VINE 105 hectares

PRODUCTION 280,000 bottles

SOIL Médoc gravel

GRAPE VARIETIES 68% Cabernet Sauvignon, 28% Merlot, 4% Petit Verdot

AGEING 14 to 16 months in barrel - New barrels: 50 - 60%

SECOND WINE Connétable Talbot

Château Talbot
33250 Saint-Julien Beychevelle
Tel.: +33 (0)5 56 73 21 50
talbot@chateau-talbot.com
www.chateau-talbot.com

@ChateauTalbot
@ChateauTalbot
@TalbotOfficial

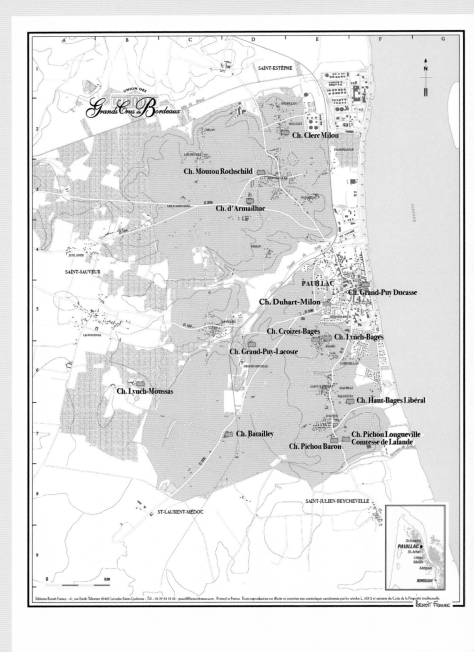

CRUS DE
PAUILLAC

Pauillac was home to a busy port from the dawn of history until the 21st century thanks to its privileged location halfway between the mouth of the Gironde Estuary and the city of Bordeaux. Many ships stopped over in Pauillac before going upriver to Bordeaux or else out to sea.

Winegrowing in Pauillac dates back to the Late Middle Ages and developed significantly over the centuries. However, it was the creation of large estates from the early 17th century to the late 19th century that gave Pauillac the importance it has today. It is also the commune with the greatest number of first growths in the 1855 classification.

PAUILLAC

Château d'Armailhac

— GRAND CRU CLASSÉ EN **1855** —

Owner: Baronne Philippine de Rothschild G.F.A.

AREA UNDER VINE 73 hectares

SOIL Gravel and clay-limestone

GRAPE VARIETIES 54 % Cabernet Sauvignon, 35% Merlot, 9% Cabernet Franc, 2% Petit Verdot

AGEING 16 months - New barrels: 40%

33250 Pauillac
Tel.: +33 (0)5 56 73 34 00

Deputy Managing Director: Philippe Dhalluin
Technical Director: Jean-Paul Polaert

webmaster@bphr.com
www.chateau-darmailhac.com

Classified a fifth growth in the 1855 classification, Château d'Armailhac borders on Château Mouton Rothschild in Pauillac, and has 73 hectares of vines planted with the finest grape varieties.

In 1933, Baron Philippe de Rothschild (1902-1988) acquired the estate – also well-known for its grounds (among the most beautiful in the Médoc), front courtyard, and château – which had belonged to the Armailhacq family since the 18th century. Known as Mouton d'Armailhacq between 1956 and 1989, the château was then successively named Mouton Baron Philippe and later Mouton Baronne Philippe.

Since 1989, Baronne Philippine de Rothschild (1933-2014) has revived the historic link with the original owner by renaming the estate Château d'Armailhac. Today, Philippe Sereys de Rothschild, Camille Sereys de Rothschild and Julien de Beaumarchais de Rothschild help maintain their ancestors' legacy and expertise.

Château Batailley

— GRAND CRU CLASSÉ EN **1855** —

Owners: The Castéja heirs

Château Batailley, listed in the 1855 classification, is one of the jewels of the Castéja family and the Borie-Manoux firm.

The name of this estate comes from the word "bataille", meaning "battle", in memory of a skirmish that took place in the vines in 1453 during the Hundred Years' War. At this time, French troops retook possession of Château Latour, which was then occupied by the English, marking the end of British troops in the Médoc.

Shaped by its rich history, the estate as we know it today was gradually transformed from the 16th to the 18th centuries. The château grounds were designed in the 19th century by Barillet-Deschamps, a famous landscape artist during the reign of Napoléon III.

This beautiful estate is planted with all Médoc grape varieties on a pure gravel terroir, producing wines characteristic of a classic Pauillac, with a deep ruby-red colour, excellent structure, and pronounced blackcurrant overtones.

AREA UNDER VINE 60 hectares

PRODUCTION 300,000 bottles

SOIL Pure gravel

GRAPE VARIETIES 70% Cabernet Sauvignon, 25% Merlot, 3% Cabernet Franc, 2% Petit Verdot

AGEING 18 months - New barrels: 50% - 60%, French oak

SECOND WINE Lions de Batailley

33250 Pauillac
Tel.: +33 (0)5 56 00 00 70
domaines@borie-manoux.fr
www.batailley.com

f Chateau Batailley
⊙ chateaubatailley
𝕏 CHBATAILLEY

Château
Clerc Milon

— GRAND CRU CLASSÉ EN 1855 —

Owner: Baronne Philippine de Rothschild G.F.A.

AREA UNDER VINE 41 hectares

SOIL Gravel and clay-limestone

GRAPE VARIETIES 52% Cabernet Sauvignon, 36% Merlot, 8% Cabernet Franc, 2% Petit Verdot, 2% Carmenère

AGEING 18 months - New barrels: 50%

SECOND WINE Pastourelle de Clerc Milon

Lieu-dit Mousset - 33250 Pauillac
Tel.: +33 (0)5 56 41 43 43

Managing Director: Jean-Emmanuel Danjoy
Deputy Managing Director: Philippe Dhalluin

visites@bphr.com
www.chateau-clerc-milon.com

Included in the famous 1855 classification, Château Clerc Milon has 41 hectares of vines overlooking the Gironde Estuary in the commune of Pauillac. This estate's wine is characterised by its rare, historical grape variety, Carmenère. A superb terroir both in terms of soil and sun exposure, it is adjacent to the first great growths of Bordeaux.

Baron Philippe de Rothschild (1902-1988) acquired Château Clerc Milon in 1970. Thanks to the dynamism of his daughter, Baroness Philippine de Rothschild (1933-2014) and a devoted team, Château Clerc Milon is gaining in quality year after year. The various changes have borne fruit, and Clerc Milon has now become one of the finest wines in the Médoc.

In 2015, the Château started producing a second wine known as Pastourelle de Clerc Milon.

Today, Philippe Sereys de Rothschild, Camille Sereys de Rothschild and Julien de Beaumarchais de Rothschild maintain the legacy and expertise of their mother, Baronne Philippine.

PAUILLAC

Château Croizet-Bages

— **GRAND CRU CLASSÉ EN 1855** —

Owner: The Quié family

CHÂTEAU
CROIZET-BAGES
GRAND CRU CLASSÉ EN 1855
PAUILLAC
2015

PAUL QUIÉ, PROPRIÉTAIRE ÉLEVEUR À PAUILLAC

Château Croizet-Bages, a great growth in the 1855 classification, takes its name from the Croizet brothers, who created the estate in the 17th century in the heart of the famous hamlet of Bages in Pauillac. The wine received special recognition at the 1878 and 1889 Universal Exhibitions, reflected in the gold medals featured on the label.

Monsieur Paul Quié clearly saw the potential of this great growth when he acquired the estate in 1942. He renovated the vineyard with dedication and patience. His son Jean-Michel, along with his grandchildren, continue his efforts, combining their experience with all the advantages of modern winemaking.

Château Croizet-Bages is a generous, opulent, and expressive wine with a very powerful bouquet reminiscent of black fruit, spice, and cedar, accompanied by a fine tannic texture on the palate.

AREA UNDER VINE 26 hectares

PRODUCTION 70,000 bottles

SOIL Deep gravel, gravelly sand

GRAPE VARIETIES 62% Cabernet Sauvignon, 28% Merlot, 6% Cabernet Franc, 4% Petit Verdot

AGEING 18 months including 12 to 14 months in barrel - New barrels: 50 - 55%

SECOND WINE ALIAS Croizet-Bages

———•———

9, rue du Port de la Verrerie - 33250 Pauillac
Tel.: +33 (0) 5 56 59 01 62

croizetbages@domaines-quie.com
www.croizetbages.fr

Château Duhart-Milon

— GRAND CRU CLASSÉ EN 1855 —

Owner: Domaines Barons de Rothschild (Lafite)

AREA UNDER VINE 75 hectares

PRODUCTION 230,000 bottles

SOIL Fine gravel mixed with aeolian sand on a limestone subsoil from the Tertiary period

GRAPE VARIETIES 67% Cabernet Sauvignon, 33% Merlot

AGEING 14 months - New barrels: 50%

SECOND WINE Moulin de Duhart

Château Duhart-Milon
33250 Pauillac
Tel.: +33 (0)5 56 73 18 18

Technical Director: Éric Kohler

visites@lafite.com
www.lafite.com

@thedomaines

Located next to Château Lafite Rothschild, Château Duhart-Milon was acquired by Domaines Barons de Rothschild (Lafite) in 1962. According to oral tradition, "Sieur Duhart" was the name of a corsair under Louis XV who settled in Pauillac when he retired. The corsair's house in the port of Pauillac inspired the label for Duhart-Milon wines. Since the early 18th century, Duhart-Milon wines served as additional income for the "Lord of Lafite" and were classified as Château Lafite's "second wine", confirming the high quality of the terroir. The 1855 classification elevated Duhart-Milon to Grand Cru Classé status in the commune of Pauillac.

The 75-hectare vineyard in the Pauillac appellation is planted with 67% Cabernet Sauvignon and 33% Merlot.

It stretches out over the west side of Château Lafite Rothschild on the Milon hillside, which runs along the Carruades de Lafite plateau.

Each vintage is aged in oak barrels from the tonnellerie des Domaines. Barrel ageing varies from 10 to 18 months, depending on the vintage.

Château Grand-Puy Ducasse

— **GRAND CRU CLASSÉ EN 1855** —

Owner: CA Grands Crus

This classified growth consists of three large vineyard plots grown on some of the finest terroir in Pauillac: the northern plot is a neighbour of Mouton and Lafite Rothschild, the central plot is located in a part of Grand-Puy, and the southern plot is on the Saint-Lambert plateau. This unusual configuration was due to the estate's founder, Pierre Ducasse.

Château Grand Puy Ducasse has entered a new phase of its history in recent vintages with a decided upswing in quality. This was largely thanks to a careful study of the potential of each individual plot. The vines are now trained higher and each different grape variety has been perfectly matched to the most suitable terroir. Ripe, healthy Cabernet Sauvignon and Merlot grapes, coupled with rigorous production and ageing methods, account for Grand Puy Ducasse's reputation for aromatic complexity, beautiful structure, and excellent ageing potential. It is the epitome of a fine Pauillac. The estate has been committed to adopting environmentally friendly practices since 2006 and has obtained HVE (High Environmental Value) certification.

AREA UNDER VINE 40 hectares

PRODUCTION 100,000 bottles

SOIL Siliceous gravel and sandy-clay gravel

GRAPE VARIETIES 63% Cabernet Sauvignon, 37% Merlot

AGEING 16 to 18 months - New barrels: 35%

SECOND WINE Prélude - Grand-Puy Ducasse

———

4 Quai Antoine Ferchaud - 33250 Pauillac
Tel.: +33 (0)5 56 59 00 40

Managing Director: Anne Le Naour

contact@cagrandscrus.fr
www.grandpuyducasse.fr

@ChateauGrandPuyDucasse
@chateaugrandpuyducasse

Château
Grand-Puy-Lacoste

— GRAND CRU CLASSÉ EN 1855 —

Owner: François-Xavier Borie

AREA UNDER VINE 62 hectares

PRODUCTION Approximately 180,000 bottles

SOIL Deep layer of large-sized gravel on a hilly rise

GRAPE VARIETIES 75% Cabernet Sauvignon, 20% Merlot, 5% Cabernet Franc

AGEING 16 to 18 months – New barrels: 75%

SECOND WINE Lacoste-Borie

BP 82 - 33250 Pauillac
Tel.: +33 (0)5 56 59 06 66

President: François-Xavier Borie
Marketing Director: Emeline Borie

dfxb@domainesfxborie.com
www.grand-puy-lacoste.com

@grandpuylacoste

Château Grand-Puy owes its name to its location on a "puy", or "hill", and the Lacoste family forged relations with the estate owner around the time the 1855 classification was established.

The estate's terroir, consisting of a single block of vines, overlooking the town of Pauillac, benefits from an outstanding hilly terrain and favourable microclimate influenced by the nearby Gironde Estuary.

The château reigns over a sea of vines. Included in the famous 1855 classification, Grand-Puy-Lacoste has played an important role in the history of Bordeaux wine since the early 16th century. Several families have taken over direction of the estate including the Lacostes and Raymond Dupins who handed it over to the Borie family in 1978.

Estate owner and manager François-Xavier Borie completely renovated the buildings to help express the unique qualities of the magnificent terroir. This great growth estate produces quintessential Pauillac wines with powerful, velvety tannin.

Château
Haut-Bages Libéral

Château
Haut-Bages
LIBÉRAL
GRAND CRU CLASSÉ
PAUILLAC

CLAIRE VILLARS LURTON

— GRAND CRU CLASSÉ EN 1855 —

Owner: Claire Villars Lurton

Château Haut-Bages Libéral was founded by the Libéral family in the 18th century. This group of wine brokers sold most of their wines to the Netherlands and Belgium. Over time, the vineyard was planted with vines from the best terroirs in the Pauillac region. As a result, half of the vines in this fifth growth estate are planted adjacent to Château Latour while the other half are located on the plateau of Bages next to Château Pichon Baron, south of Pauillac.

Since the acquisition of the estate by the Merlaut family in 1983, Claire Villars Lurton undertook to reform vineyard operations in 2000, followed by a complete renovation in 2018.

Conscious of the estate's legacy, she naturally chose to produce the wines using sustainable viticultural methods.

The estate, which began growing half of its wines biodynamically in 2008, has now undergone a complete conversion to organic and biodynamic vineyard management.

AREA UNDER VINE 28 hectares

PRODUCTION 80,000 bottles

SOIL Garonne Günz gravel on a clay-limestone subsoil

GRAPE VARIETIES 72% Cabernet Sauvignon, 28% Merlot

AGEING 16 months - New barrels: 45%

SECOND WINE La Chapelle de Haut Bages Libéral

Saint Lambert - 33250 Pauillac
Tel.: +33 (0)5 56 59 11 88

Production Manager: Thomas Bontemps

infos@hautbagesliberal.com
www.hautbagesliberal.com

 @chateauhautbagesliberal
 @chateauHBL
 chateau_hautbagesliberal

Château Lynch-Bages

— GRAND CRU CLASSÉ EN **1855** —

Owner: The Cazes family

AREA UNDER VINE 100 hectares

PRODUCTION 300,000 bottles

SOIL Caronne gravel

GRAPE VARIETIES 70% Cabernet Sauvignon, 24% Merlot, 4% Cabernet Franc, 2% Petit Verdot

AGEING 18 months in French oak barrels - New barrels: 70%

SECOND WINE Echo de Lynch-Bages

33250 - Pauillac
Tel.: +33 (0)5 56 73 24 00

Managing Director: Jean-Charles Cazes

contact@lynchbages.com
www.famillejmcazes.com

LynchBagesPauillac
chateaulynchbages
lynch_bages

Overlooking the Gironde Estuary, Château Lynch-Bages is a great growth in the 1855 classification located on a magnificent gravelly rise on the outskirts of Pauillac. The estate formerly belonged to the Lynch family, originally from Ireland, and was purchased by Jean-Charles Cazes in 1939. Housed in a 16th-century building, the old vat room dates back to the 1850s. It is one of the rare remaining winemaking facilities of its kind. A visit is truly a trip back in time...

In 2017, the family began a new chapter in the estate's history by renovating its winemaking facilities. In-depth soil surveys have been undertaken in the vineyard for several years, and the renovation project, headed by American architect Chien Chung Pei, naturally fits into the estate's quest for excellence.

The estate will offer tours of its new cellars in 2020!

Château Lynch-Moussas

— GRAND CRU CLASSÉ EN 1855 —

Owners: The Castéja heirs

Lynch-Moussas is a historic estate purchased by the Lynch family and formerly located on three large plateaux: Madrac, Moussas, and Bages. In the 19th century, the estate was divided into two: Bages Jurine (today Lynch-Bages) and Lynch-Moussas (named after the plateau where many of the vines are grown).

Pauillac land owners since the 17th century, the Castéja family acquired Château Lynch-Moussas in the early 20th century. Émile Castéja inherited the estate, as well as management, in 1970 and immediately set about enhancing its development. His son, Philippe Castéja, has managed this and all the family's other estates since 2001.

This date coincides with the creation of a second wine, Les Hauts de Lynch-Moussas.

Château Lynch-Moussas wine is sold on the Bordeaux marketplace.

GRAND CRU CLASSÉ EN 1855

CHATEAU LYNCH-MOUSSAS

PAUILLAC

2015

AREA UNDER VINE 62 hectares

PRODUCTION 200,000 bottles

SOIL Pure gravel

GRAPE VARIETIES 75% Cabernet Sauvignon, 25% Merlot

AGEING 18 months - New barrels: 55%

SECOND WINE Les Hauts de Lynch-Moussas

—•—

Château Lynch-Moussas - 33250 Pauillac
Tel.: +33 (0)5 56 00 00 70

domaines@borie-manoux.fr
www.lynch-moussas.com

Chateau Lynch Moussas

chateaulynchmoussas

Château
Pichon Baron

— GRAND CRU CLASSÉ EN 1855 —

Owner: AXA MILLESIMES

AREA UNDER VINE 73 hectares

SOIL Deep gravel

GRAPE VARIETIES 65% Cabernet Sauvignon, 30% Merlot, 3% Cabernet Franc, 2% Petit Verdot

AGEING 18 months - New barrels: 80% (1st wine)

SECOND WINE
Les Tourelles de Longueville

———•———

Château Pichon-Longueville Baron
33250 Pauillac
Tel.: +33 (0)5 56 73 17 17

General Director of AXA Millésimes:
Christian Seely
Technical Director: Jean-René Matignon

contact@pichonbaron.com
www.pichonbaron.com

PichonBaron
pichonbaron

Château Pichon Baron is a second growth in the 1855 classification and a historic Bordeaux estate.

The great terroir, located on a slope at the Pichon Baron estate, is a historic plot that has produced wine since 1694. It is dedicated to producing the estate's first wine, constituting the majority of the blend.

The grapes used to produce Château Pichon Baron wines are meticulously selected in the vineyard and cellar. The unique terroir finds its purest expression in the wine's long aftertaste, power and perfect balance between finesse and elegance.

Built in 1851, the château features slender turrets reflected in a water mirror and benefits from breathtaking views over the Gironde Estuary. Our main priorities include organising various events and opening up the estate to wine enthusiasts around the world.

Château Pichon Longueville Comtesse de Lalande

— **GRAND CRU CLASSÉ EN 1855** —

Owner: M. Frédéric Rouzaud
Louis Roederer Champagne House

Château Pichon Longueville Comtesse de Lalande has an outstanding 90-hectare terroir ideally located in Pauillac on the banks of the Gironde Estuary.

Despite its long, rich history, only four families have owned the emblematic Médoc estate, with the Louis Roederer Champagne House injecting an ambitious, innovative dynamism in 2007.

From the vineyard's gradual conversion towards biodynamic methods to the installation of state-of-the-art winemaking facilities, every effort has been made to help the Pichon Comtesse terroir produce well-balanced, classy, and elegant Pauillac wines.

AREA UNDER VINE 90 hectares

PRODUCTION 170,000 bottles

SOIL Garonne gravel on a clay subsoil with traces of ironpan

GRAPE VARIETIES 62% Cabernet Sauvignon, 28% Merlot, 7% Cabernet Franc, 3% Petit Verdot

AGEING 18 months in barrel - New barrels: 60%

SECOND WINE La Réserve de la Comtesse

Route des châteaux - 33250 Pauillac
Tel.: +33 (0) 56 59 19 40

Managing Director: Nicolas Glumineau
Marketing and Sales Director: Charles Fournier

pichon@pichon-comtesse.com
www.pichon-comtesse.com

 @pichon_comtesse

 #pichoncomtesse

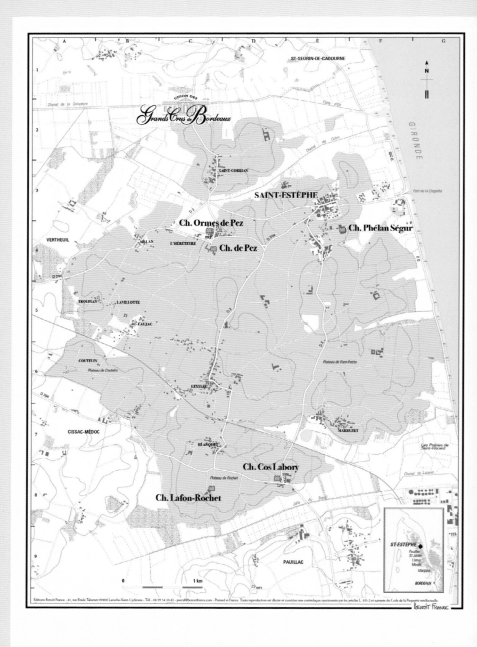

CRUS DE
SAINT-ESTÈPHE

Saint-Estèphe is the northernmost appellation in the Haut-Médoc. It benefits from an outstanding location along the Gironde Estuary, which can be seen from most of the commune's gravelly rises.

The first known inhabitants date back to the Bronze Age, and vines were planted here during the Roman occupation at the beginning of the Common Era.

The 17th, 18th and 19th centuries saw the development of grands crus which, as in the other famous communal appellations in the Médoc and helped by the Bordeaux négociants who aged and sold the wines, contributed greatly to the reputation of Saint-Estèphe around the world.

SAINT-ESTÈPHE

Château
Cos Labory

— GRAND CRU CLASSÉ EN **1855** —

Owner: SCE des Domaines Audoy

AREA UNDER VINE 18 hectares

PRODUCTION 80,000 bottles

SOIL Günz gravel on a marl-limestone bedrock

GRAPE VARIETIES 36% Merlot, 58% Cabernet Sauvignon, 6% Petit Verdot

AGEING 14 months in French oak barrels - New barrels: 50%

SECOND WINE Charme de Cos Labory

33180 Saint-Estèphe
Tel.: +33 (0)5 56 59 30 22

Manager: Bernard Audoy

contact@cos-labory.com
www.cos-labory.com

Cos Labory owes its name to the word "caux", meaning "stony hill" and to François Labory, who owned the estate from 1820 to 1840. Purchased in 1845 by Monsieur d'Estournel, Château Cos Labory was sold in 1852 to Charles Martyns, an English banker. This great growth is included in the famous 1855 classification and has belonged to the Audoy family for over half a century.

The eighteen-hectare vineyard is located on the famous gravelly rise of Cos and benefits from remarkable sun exposure. It is planted with traditional grape varieties.

Major investments over the past several years have enabled Château Cos Labory to benefit from the latest technology to produce its wines.

Meticulous care and attention is taken in the cellar, where the wines are fermented and aged, tailored to the characteristics of each vintage. Cos Labory is a powerful yet elegant wine with the classic structure of a Saint-Estèphe wines.

SAINT-ESTÈPHE

Château Lafon-Rochet

— GRAND CRU CLASSÉ EN 1855 —

Owners: M. Michel Tesseron and Mme Caroline Poniatowski

The history of Château Lafon-Rochet dates back to the mid-16th century. The estate belonged to the Lafon family for over two centuries, who were able to keep hold of it through the turmoil of the French Revolution. They also lived to see its ultimate recognition in the 1855 classification.

Lafon-Rochet was thus admitted to the exclusive great growth club, one of only five estates to do so in Saint-Estèphe. Ideally located between Cos d'Estournel and Lafite-Rothschild to the south, Lafon-Rochet sits next to some of the finest vineyards in the world. It is not hard to see why Guy Tesseron, well-known for the quality of his old Cognac, was interested in purchasing the estate over forty years ago.

Continuous efforts in the vineyard and cellar have helped make Lafon-Rochet become one of the finest wines in Saint-Estèphe, France, and the whole world.

AREA UNDER VINE 40 hectares

SOIL Deep gravel and clay-gravel

GRAPE VARIETIES 57% Cabernet Sauvignon, 36% Merlot, 4% Petit Verdot, 3% Cabernet Franc

AGEING 15 months - New barrels: 50%

SECOND WINE Les Pèlerins de Lafon-Rochet

———•———

Blanquet Ouest - 33180 Saint-Estèphe
Tel.: +33 (0)5 56 59 32 06

Managing Director: Basile Tesseron

Email : lafon@lafon-rochet.com
Site web : www.lafon-rochet.com

Château Lafon Rochet

chateau_lafonrochet

SAINT-ESTÈPHE

159

Château Ormes De Pez

Owner: The Cazes family

AREA UNDER VINE 40 hectares

PRODUCTION 200,000 bottles

SOIL Garonne gravel

GRAPE VARIETIES 48% Cabernet Sauvignon, 42% Merlot, 8% Cabernet Franc, 2% Petit Verdot

AGEING 14 to 16 months - New barrels: 45%

Route des Ormes - 33180 Saint-Estèphe
Tel.: +33 (0)5 56 73 24 00

Managing Director: Jean-Charles Cazes

contact@ormesdepez.com
www.famillejmcazes.com

Château Ormes de Pez dates back to the 18th century. Located on the edge of the hamlet of Pez, west of Saint-Estèphe, the estate owes its name to a magnificent group of elm trees which have since disappeared. Alongside Château Lynch-Bages, Château Ormes de Pez is the second estate acquired by Jean-Charles Cazes in 1939 on the eve of the Second World War.

Special attention is paid to vineyard management practices, particularly with regard to winemaking and ageing techniques, in order to produce wines to the highest standards. Les Ormes de Pez has a spicy, voluptuous flavour with good tannic structure. The estate also has five guest rooms with a privileged, calm atmosphere.

Château Ormes de Pez has everything it takes to make great wine, while offering visitors a charming stay in the heart of the wine country.

Château de Pez

GRAND VIN

CHÂTEAU DE PEZ

2015

SAINT-ESTÈPHE
APPELLATION SAINT-ESTÈPHE CONTRÔLÉE

Owner: M. Frédéric Rouzaud
The Louis Roederer Champagne House

Château de Pez is one of the oldest estates in the appellation, dating back to 1454. Over the years, it has established itself as a winegrowing estate, and undergone an architectural renovation in keeping with the Château's 18th century style.

The Louis Roederer Champagne House bought the beautiful, historic estate in 1995.

2018 marked a new beginning for Château de Pez, with the installation of stainless-steel vats, making it possible to fine-tune winemaking on a plot-by-plot basis.

Located west of Saint-Estèphe, the estate comprises 48 hectares of vines planted on gravel soil on a clay-limestone bedrock overlooking the Gironde Estuary. The wines of Château de Pez are powerful, classy, and velvety with a beautiful tannic structure, long aftertaste, and excellent ageing potential.

AREA UNDER VINE 48 hectares

PRODUCTION 200,000 bottles

SOIL Limestone gravel and clay

GRAPE VARIETIES 47% Cabernet Sauvignon, 44% Merlot, 6% Cabernet Franc, 3% Petit Verdot

AGEING 12 to 15 months - New barrels: 40%

Lieu-dit Pez - 33180 Saint-Estèphe
Tel.: +33 (05) 56 59 30 26

Managing Director: Nicolas Glumineau
Marketing and Sales Director: Charles Fournier

com@champagne-roederer.com
www.chateaudepez.com

@chateaudepez

#chateaudepez

Château
Phélan Ségur

Owner: Philippe Van de Vyvere

AREA UNDER VINE 70 hectares

PRODUCTION 350,000 bottles

SOIL Clay-gravel

GRAPE VARIETIES 58% Cabernet Sauvignon, 39% Merlot, 1.5% Petit Verdot, 1,5% Cabernet Franc

AGEING 18 months - New barrels: 50%

SECOND WINE Frank Phélan

33180 Saint Estèphe
Tel.: +33 (0)5 56 59 74 00

Managing Director: Véronique Dausse

phelan@phelansegur.com
www.phelansegur.com

f @château Phélan Ségur

◎ @phelansegur

♪ @phelan_segur

微 波尔多飞龙世家**Veronique**

Founded by the Irishman Bernard Phélan and developed by his son, Frank, Château Phélan Ségur has been one of the benchmarks of the Saint-Estèphe appellation since the 19th century.

Consisting of seventy hectares of vines divided into four distinct parts, the estate benefits from a heterogeneous terroir which accounts for Phélan Ségur's unique complexity.

The cellar and vat room are integrated into the château in a highly unusual architectural ensemble.

The wines are aged with the greatest of care and Phélan Ségur is famous for its elegance, finesse, and balance.

In 2018, the Gardinier family handed the reins to the great Bordeaux wine enthusiast Philippe Van de Vyvere.

Philippe Van de Vyvere applies his entrepreneurial values to making the finest wine possible from both an aesthetic and a technical standpoint, with great respect of the environment.

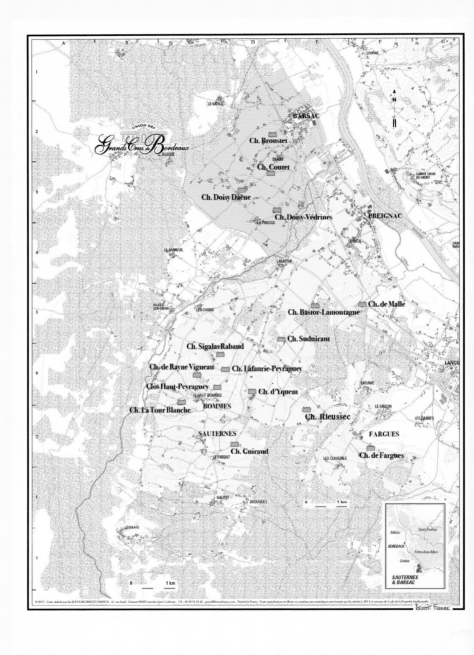

UNION DES
Grands Crus de Bordeaux

LOUPIAC

BARSAC

Ch. Broustet

Ch. Coutet

Ch. Doisy Daëne

Ch. Doisy-Védrines

PREIGNAC

Ch. de Malle

Ch. Bastor-Lamontagne

Ch. Suduiraut

Ch. Sigalas Rabaud

Ch. de Rayne Vigneau

Ch. Lafaurie-Peyraguey

Clos Haut-Peyraguey

Ch. d'Yquem

Ch. La Tour Blanche

BOMMES

Ch. Rieussec

SAUTERNES

FARGUES

Ch. Guiraud

Ch. de Fargues

0   1 km

0   1 km

Médoc   Saint-Émilion

BORDEAUX   Entre-deux-Mers

Graves

SAUTERNES
& BARSAC

BENOIT FRANCE

CRUS DE
SAUTERNES OR BARSAC

The Sauternes appellation consists of five communes: Sauternes, Fargues, Bommes, Preignac, and Barsac. Barsac has its own separate appellation as well.

Sauternes is considered the finest white wine in the world by many connoisseurs. The jewel of Sauternes, Château d'Yquem, was the only estate in either the Médoc or Sauternes to be classified a "Premier Cru Supérieur" in 1855.

The appellation is separated from the Graves on its western side by the Ciron valley. The river Ciron is responsible for the microclimate particularly conducive to *Botrytis cinerea*, a fungus that concentrates the grapes and produces outstanding wines.

Château
Bastor-Lamontagne

Owner: Joseph Helfrich

AREA UNDER VINE 52 hectares

PRODUCTION 60,000 to 80,000 bottles

SOIL Siliceous gravel on a limestone subsoil

GRAPE VARIETIES 80% Sémillon, 20% Sauvignon

AGEING 16 months - New barrels: 30%

SECOND WINE Les Remparts de Bastor-Lamontagne

Domaine de Lamontagne - 33210 Preignac
Tel.: +33 (0)5 56 63 27 66

President: Joseph Helfrich
Technical Director: Vincent Cachau

vgarat@bastorlamontagne.com
www.bastor-lamontagne.com

 bastorlamontagne
 chateau_bastor_lamontagne
 @chateaubastor

Located in Preignac, one of five communes in the Sauternes appellation, Château Bastor-Lamontagne has 52 hectares of vineyards in a single block on siliceous-gravel soil, accounting for the wine's richness and fine tannic structure.

The estate takes its name from Chevalier de la Montaigne, a councillor of the Bordeaux Parliament who become the owner in 1711. Indicated on Belleyme's famous map dating back to the late 18th century, Bastore was considered a high-ranking estate from the outset. The château's golden age, however, came in the 19th century under the management of Amédée Larrieu, who also owned Château Haut-Brion in Pessac.

Château Bastor-Lamontagne has always prized itself on making fruity, well-balanced wines: Often referred to as "modern Sauternes", the estate's classy wines make them suited to all occasions. Although it can age very well, Bastor-Lamontagne is also delicious young thanks to its vivaciousness and elegance.

SAUTERNES

Château Broustet

— GRAND CRU CLASSÉ EN 1855 —

Owner: Vignobles de Terroirs

Monsieur Capdeville, owner of Chateau Broustet, acquired the neighbouring estate, Chateau Nairac in the early 19th century. It was consequently referred to as "Broustet-Nairac" when it was ranked a second growth in the 1855 classification.

The Fournier family acquired Chateau Broustet in the late 19th century and set up a cooperage there. The model for the 225-litre "barrique bordelaise", or "Bordeaux barrel" is said to have been created at Broustet, an explanation backed up by documents in the archives of the Bordeaux Chamber of Commerce. This magnificent estate, located in Barsac, has belonged to Vignobles de Terroirs since 2010.

At the end of summer, morning mists warmed by the sun are conducive to the early and slow development of noble rot. The pebbles and scattered topazes store the sun's heat and release it at night, which is ideal for producing overripe grapes. These are picked by hand in several passes, resulting in an outstanding wine.

AREA UNDER VINE 17 hectares
PRODUCTION 15,000 bottles
SOIL Clay-limestone and alluvial gravel
GRAPE VARIETIES 70% Sémillon, 20% Sauvignon, 10% Muscadelle
AGEING 22 months - New barrels: 40%
SECOND WINE Les Charmes de Château Broustet

———•———

33720 Barsac
Tel.: +33 (0)5 47 74 78 00

President of the Estate: Pierre Mauget
S.C.E.A Manager: Jean-Hubert Beaupuy

broustet@vignoblesdeterroirs.com
www.vignoblesdeterroirs.com

SAUTERNES OR BARSAC

Château Coutet

— PREMIER GRAND CRU CLASSÉ EN 1855 —

Owners: Philippe and Dominique Baly

AREA UNDER VINE 38.5 hectares

PRODUCTION 42,000 bottles

SOIL Clay-limestone

GRAPE VARIETIES 75% Sémillon, 23% Sauvignon Blanc, 2% Muscadelle

AGEING 18 months in French oak barrels - New barrels: 90% - 100%

SECOND WINE La Chartreuse de Coutet

Lieu dit Château Coutet - 33720 Barsac
Tel.: +33 (0)5 56 27 15 46

Manager: Philippe Baly
Marketing and Communications Director:
Aline Baly

info@chateaucoutet.com
www.chateaucoutet.com

 Château Coutet à Barsac, 1er Grand Cru Classé

 @ChateauCoutet et @ ChateauCoutetaBarsac

 @ChateauCoutet

Recognised as one of the finest wines in its appellation, Château Coutet was ranked a first growth in 1855. Coutet is one of the oldest estates in the Sauternes region and has an outstanding architectural heritage and terroir. Château Coutet belonged to the Lur Saluces family for over a century and is currently owned and managed by Philippe and Dominique Baly, with technical and commercial assistance from Baron Philippe de Rothschild S.A., who have exclusive distribution rights.

The name "Coutet" comes from the Gascon word for "couteau", meaning "knife", in reference to the wine's fresh, vibrant acidity and unique crispness. When young, Château Coutet has aromas of white flowers, citrus, honey, and vanilla. Noble rot comes through with age, revealing a deep, delicate bouquet with hints of spice and candied fruit.

Château
Doisy Daëne

— GRAND CRU CLASSÉ EN 1855 —

Owners: Fabrice and Jean-Jacques Dubourdieu

Château Doisy-Daëne, included among the second growths in the 1855 classification, is located in Barsac in the Sauternes appellation and has belonged to the Dubourdieu family since 1924. Four generations of winegrowers, from father to son, have made sweet white wines here for over eighty years: Georges (1924-1948), Pierre (1949-1999), Denis (2000-2016), followed by Jean-Jacques and Fabrice since 2016.

The wines have their own special style, with bright fruit concentrated by "noble rot" as well as lively acidity, excellent balance, and delicate flavours. Doisy-Daëne's style reflects both its excellent limestone terroir and long family tradition for producing high-quality, classy white wines that are powerful, fresh, and irrevocably young with a diamond-like purity.

AREA UNDER VINE 18 hectares

PRODUCTION 25,000 bottles

SOIL Red sand (Barsac) on a limestone subsoil

GRAPE VARIETIES 86% Sémillon, 13% Sauvignon Blanc, 1% Muscadelle

AGEING 10 months - New barrels: 30%

———•———

EARL Denis Dubourdieu Domaines
Château Doisy Daëne, 15 Gravas - 33720 Barsac
Tel.: +33 (0)5 56 62 96 51

Manager: Jean-Jacques Dubourdieu

contact@denisdubourdieu.fr
www.denisdubourdieu.fr

Château Doisy-Védrines

— **GRAND CRU CLASSÉ EN 1855** —

Owners: The Pierre Casteja heirs

AREA UNDER VINE 36 hectares

PRODUCTION 40,000 to 50,000 bottles, depending on the vintage

SOIL Clay-limestone

GRAPE VARIETIES 80% Sémillon, 10% Sauvignon Blanc, 5% Sauvignon Gris, 5% Muscadelle

AGEING 18 months in barrel for the first wine; 12 months in barrel for the second wine - New barrels: 60% French oak barrels

SECOND WINE Château Petit Vedrines

Château Doisy-Védrines - 33720 Barsac
Tel.: 33 (0)5 56 27 15 13

Manager: Olivier Casteja
Managing Director: Frédéric Deyres

doisy-vedrines@orange.fr

 chateau_doisyvedrines

The Chevaliers de Védrines owned this estate for centuries and gave their name to it.

Included in the 1855 classification, it was acquired by the present owners in the mid-19th century.

Doisy-Védrines is located on a clay-limestone plateau in Haut-Barsac. The soil is ploughed using traditional methods and the grapes are picked by hand in 6 or 8 passes. Fermentation and ageing take place exclusively in French oak barrels.

The combination of modern and traditional winemaking techniques gives Château Doisy-Védrines its trademark freshness and finesse typical of the finest wines of Barsac. Annual production varies from 36,000 to 40,000 bottles depending on the vintage.

When young, the wine is well-balanced and particularly delicious as an aperitif. Older vintages are a delight at the end of a meal.

SAUTERNES

Château de Fargues

Owner: Marquis de Lur Saluces

Château de Fargues, located in the prestigious Sauternes appellation, has belonged to the Lur Saluces family since 1472, and serves as a unique example of a single family's long, unbroken ownership. The family's history is intimately linked to the region and its wine.

The first Fargues vintage dates back to 1943, which explains why it was not listed in the 1855 classification. Since it is outside the classification, Fargues is a fine wine that is unclassifiable. In just over 70 years, Château de Fargues has established a reputation as one of the most successful wines in the appellation.

The grapes are harvested meticulously in several passes and ageing takes place in barrels for thirty months to produce a wine of rare complexity, with remarkably long ageing potential, which stands among the estate's greatest wines. Quality always prevails, and we do our utmost to capture the tremendous aromatics of Lur Saluces wines and put them into bottle.

AREA UNDER VINE 21 hectares

PRODUCTION 20,000 bottles

SOIL Clay-gravel

GRAPE VARIETIES 80% Sémillon, 20% Sauvignon

AGEING 30 months - New barrels: 40%

33210 Fargues de Langon
Tel.: +33 (0)5 57 98 04 20

Co-managers: Marquis de Lur Saluces and Count Philippe de Lur Saluces
Operations Manager: François Amirault

fargues@chateaudefargues.com
www.chateaudefargues.com

🐦 @chateau_fargues

SAUTERNES OR BARSAC

171

Château Guiraud

— **PREMIER GRAND CRU CLASSÉ EN 1855** —

Owner: SCA Château Guiraud

AREA UNDER VINE 105 hectares

PRODUCTION 90,000 bottles

SOIL Sandy gravel and deep clay

GRAPE VARIETIES 65% Sémillon, 35 % Sauvignon Blanc

AGEING 18 to 24 months in barrel - New barrels: 100%

SECOND WINE Petit Guiraud

33210 Sauternes
Tel.: +33 (0)5 56 76 61 01

Manager: Xavier Planty

accueil@chateauguiraud.com
www.chateauguiraud.com

chateauguiraud
#chateauguiraud
chateau_guiraud

Château Guiraud has gained a reputation for shaping its own destiny. It is one of the rarest in France to have created a conservatory of grape varieties. Vineyard management practices experienced a cultural revolution since 1996, when owners decided to steer the estate towards biodiversity. Château Guiraud became the first great growth in the 1855 classification to obtain organic certification in 2011.

Since 1766, Château Guiraud has combined reinvention with non-conformism to cultural and political norms, with an ongoing focus on producing outstanding wines. The "Guiraud" merchant family established the mysterious reputation of the château, while the estate's black label sanctifies protestant and republican values.

Today Château Guiraud is owned by four wine enthusiasts who teamed up in 2006: the Peugeot family holding company represented by Robert Peugeot and three winegrowers: Olivier Bernard, Stephan von Neipperg and Xavier Planty, estate manager since 1986.

SAUTERNES OR BARSAC

SAUTERNES

Clos Haut-Peyraguey

— PREMIER GRAND CRU CLASSÉ EN 1855 —

Owner: Bernard Magrez

Peyraguey, whose name means a hill or promontory, is an ancient barony acquired during the 18th century by the President of the Bordeaux Parliament who was beheaded during the French Revolution. The estate was then acquired by Monsieur Lafaurie, followed by Monsieur Saint Rieul Dupouy, and later Count Duchatel in 1864. Following the death of Count Duchatel in 1879, the estate was divided into two parts and Clos Haut-Peyraguey was established. Clos Haut-Peyraguey is the smallest of the Sauternes first growths and the highest part of the vineyard, Haut-Bommes, has an outstanding terroir. The estate was then acquired by Parisian pharmacist Monsieur Grillon and handed over to the Pauly family in 1914. In late 2012, Bernard Magrez acquired this Sauternes Premier Grand Cru Classé and thus became the only estate owner of four great growths in Bordeaux.

AREA UNDER VINE 21 hectares

PRODUCTION 20,000 bottles

SOIL Sandy-gravel on a clay subsoil

GRAPE VARIETIES 93% Sémillon, 7% Sauvignon White

AGEING 20 months - New barrels: 30 - 40%

SECOND WINE Symphonie de Haut-Peyraguey

1, Haut-Peyraguey - 33210 Bommes
Tel.: +33 (0)5 56 76 61 53

Director: Anthony Defives

closhautpeyraguey@pape-clement.com
www.bernard-magrez.com

ClosHautPeyraguey
bernardmagrez
bernardmagrez
bernardmagrez
Bernard Magrez

CHÂTEAU
LAFAURIE-PEYRAGUEY

1ᵉʳ GRAND CRU CLASSÉ
SAUTERNES

Château Lafaurie-Peyraguey

— PREMIER GRAND CRU CLASSÉ EN 1855 —

Owner: Silvio Denz

AREA UNDER VINE 36 hectares

PRODUCTION 40,000 bottles

SOIL Clay-gravel, clay and sand

GRAPE VARIETIES 93% Sémillon, 6% Sauvignon, 1% Muscadelle

AGEING 18 months - New barrels: 40%

SECOND WINE La Chapelle de Lafaurie-Peyraguey

Lieu-Dit Peyraguey - 33210 Bommes
Tel.: +33 (0)5 56 76 60 54

Managing Director: David Bolzan

info@chateau-lafaurie-peyraguey.com
www.chateau-lafaurie-peyraguey.com

Chateau.Lafaurie.Peyraguey

chateaulafauriepeyraguey

Lafaurie-Peyraguey is located on an upper gravel terrace 70 metres above sea level in Sauternes.

The L'Enclos and Maisons Rouges plots represent the historic heart of the estate's terroir, consisting of gravel from the Quaternary period, deposited over 600,000 years ago on a limestone substratum.

The winemaking facilities benefit from specially-adapted equipment conforming to the latest environmental and regulatory standards and feature fully air-conditioned cellars with controlled humidity.

Château Lafaurie-Peyraguey reflects Silvio Denz's passionate devotion to his work. He makes outstanding engraved bottles, inspired by the work of René Lalique.

"Femme et Raisins", created in 1928, was engraved in the woodwork of Pullman-Express sleeping cars, which were put into service in 1929. This engraving has appeared on Château Lafaurie-Peyraguey bottles from the 2013 vintage onwards.

SAUTERNES OR BARSAC

Château de Malle

— **GRAND CRU CLASSÉ EN 1855** —

Owner: Comtesse de Bournazel

Dating back to 1540, Château de Malle has always remained in the same family, with five generations of de Malle, six of de Lur Saluces and three of de Bournazel. The château and its Italian gardens embody all that is noble about wine and have been listed as historic monuments. A tour of this beautiful historic monument, like no other in Southwest France, is highly recommended.

Comprising some two hundred hectares, the estate is unusual in that it straddles both the Sauternes and Graves (red and white) appellations.

Château de Malle is listed in the 1855 classification. Its light sandy, gravelly soil produces intensely fruity wines. Château de Malle is rich, distinguished, and relatively light. Particularly aromatic when young, it features hints of ripe apricot, lime blossom, and acacia honey. The wine is very open for the first five or six years after the vintage before becoming closed. It generally requires another ten years to reach its peak.

AREA UNDER VINE 25 hectares

PRODUCTION 40,000 bottles

SOIL Siliceous clay-gravel

GRAPE VARIETIES 69% Sémillon, 28% Sauvignon Blanc, 3% Muscadelle

AGEING 18 to 24 months - New barrels: 30%

SECOND WINE Les Fleurs de Malle

———•———

Route du château de Malle - 33210 Preignac
Tel.: +33 (0)5 56 62 36 86

Managing Director: Paul-Henry de Bournazel
Reception: Cathy Maurey

accueil@chateau-de-malle.fr
www.chateaudemalle.com

1er Grand Cru Classé

CHÂTEAU DE RAYNE VIGNEAU

SAUTERNES

Château
de Rayne Vigneau

— **PREMIER GRAND CRU CLASSÉ EN 1855** —

Owner: Financière Trésor du Patrimoine

AREA UNDER VINE 84 hectares

PRODUCTION 35 to 40,000 bottles

SOIL Clay-gravel

GRAPE VARIETIES 70% Sémillon, 30% Sauvignon, and a hint of Muscadelle

AGEING Fermentation and ageing in French oak barrels for 18-24 months - New barrels: 30%

SECOND WINE Madame de Rayne

---

4 le Vigneau - 33210 Bommes
Tel.: + 33(0)5 56 76 61 63
and +33 (0)5 56 76 64 05 (visites)

Manager: Derek Rémy Smith
Managing Director: Vincent Labergère

chateau@raynevigneau.fr
www.raynevigneau.fr

@ChateaudeRayneVigneau
@raynevigneau
@RayneVigneau

Benefiting from a splendid terroir, Château de Rayne Vigneau has recently improved the quality of its wines, restoring them to their former 19th century glory as one of the leading Sauternes wines. This prestigious estate, located on a rise in the commune of Bommes, benefits from a rich and precious terroir scattered with agate, topaz, amethyst and sapphire, ideal for growing Sauternes and dry white wines.

Thanks to improvements undertaken at Château de Rayne Vigneau in the 2000s, Derek Rémy Smith's company Financière Trésor du Patrimoine continues its quest to make excellent wines grown on great terroirs. Vincent Labergère, an agricultural engineer and lover of Sauternes wines, has recently injected a new quality-oriented, commercial dynamism into the estate.

Château Rieussec

— **PREMIER GRAND CRU CLASSÉ EN 1855** —

Owner: Domaines Barons de Rothschild (Lafite)

Located in the heart of Sauternes, Château Rieussec has been owned by Domaines Barons de Rothschild (Lafite) since 1984. In the 18th century, the Rieussec estate belonged to the Carmelite monks in Langon, and was ranked a Premier Grand Cru in Sauternes and Barsac.

The 85-hectare vineyard is planted with Sémillon (81%), Sauvignon Blanc (17%), and Muscadelle (2%). Each vintage is aged in oak barrels, coming primarily from the tonnellerie des Domaines. Barrel ageing varies from 16 to 26 months, depending on the vintage.

AREA UNDER VINE 85 hectares

PRODUCTION Varies greatly depending on the vintage, producing on average 72,000 bottles

SOIL Sandy-clay gravel

GRAPE VARIETIES 81% Sémillon, 17% Sauvignon, 2% Muscadelle

AGEING 18 to 26 months depending on the vintage - New barrels: 80 - 100%

SECOND WINE Carmes de Rieussec

Château Rieussec
33210 Fargues
Tel.: +33 (0)5 57 98 14 14

Technical Director: Éric Kohler
Estate Manager: Jean de Roquefeuil

rieussec@lafite.com
www.lafite.com

@thedomaines

CHATEAU
SIGALAS RABAUD
PREMIER CRU CLASSÉ 1855

SAUTERNES

Château
Sigalas Rabaud

— **PREMIER GRAND CRU CLASSÉ EN 1855** —

Owner: The Lambert des Granges family

AREA UNDER VINE 14 hectares

PRODUCTION 15,000 bottles

SOIL Clay-gravel

GRAPE VARIETIES 85% Sémillon, 15% Sauvignon

AGEING 18 months - New barrels: 25%

SECOND WINE Lieutenant de Sigalas

Château Sigalas Rabaud -33210 Bommes
Tel.: +33 (0)5 57 31 07 45

Managers: Laure de Lambert Compeyrot
and Marquis Gérard de Lambert des Granges

contact@chateau-sigalas-rabaud.com
www.chateau-sigalas-rabaud.com

Château Sigalas Rabaud
Château Sigalas Rabaud

For six generations, the Sigalas family have put their heart and soul into making wine from this outstanding terroir, the smallest of the first growths, consisting of 14 hectares of vines in a single block. The estate, located between Château d'Yquem and the Ciron River, on a south-facing clay-gravel rise is where the Marquis de Lambert des Granges and his daughter, Laure, produce fine, fresh, and elegant Sauternes. These wines are refined and delicious when young, with a bouquet of lime blossom and white fruit, although they can often age for over a century.

The second wine, Lieutenant de Sigalas, is the first growth's "little brother" and is the result of a meticulous selection, combining the prestige of a fine wine with a remarkable freshness.

This great terroir also produces two excellent dry white wines, Sémillante de Sigalas, made from old Sémillon vines, and Demoiselle de Sigalas, a blend of Sémillon and Sauvignon Blanc.

At the forefront of innovation, the Sigalas team produce a wine from 100% botrytised grapes with no added sulphur, labelled "le 5 de Sigalas".

Château Suduiraut

— **PREMIER GRAND CRU CLASSÉ EN 1855** —

Owner: AXA MILLESIMES

Château Suduiraut is unanimously considered one of the leading Sauternes thanks to an extreme emphasis on quality and an enthusiastic winemaking team who work closely together to make one of the greatest wines in the world. The wine is made using a combination of plot-by-plot vineyard management, picking berry by berry, and a perfect command of fermentation in barrel and rigorous sorting during blending.

Château Suduiraut is made from the most prestigious terroirs and seduces with its outstanding ageing potential and floral, fruity aromas of very ripe, botrytised grapes. The wine's perfect elegance is the result of a well-balanced, powerful alliance between its full-bodied texture, mineral freshness, and hot, spicy flavours.

In keeping with 17th century traditions, the château is situated majestically in the heart of the vineyard and surrounded by magnificent gardens designed by Le Nôtre.

AREA UNDER VINE 91 hectares

SOIL Sandy-clay gravel

GRAPE VARIETIES 90% Sémillon, 10% Sauvignon Blanc

AGEING 18 to 24 months - New barrels: 50% (1st wine)

SECOND WINE Castelnau de Suduiraut

Château Suduiraut - 33210 Preignac
Tel.: +33 (0)5 56 63 61 92

General Director of AXA Millésimes: Christian Seely
Technical Director: Pierre Montégut

contact@suduiraut.com
www.suduiraut.com

 ChateauSuduiraut
 chateausuduiraut

Château
La Tour Blanche

— **PREMIER GRAND CRU CLASSÉ EN 1855** —

Owner: Regional Council of Nouvelle-Aquitaine

AREA UNDER VINE 40 hectares

PRODUCTION 30,000 bottles

SOIL Gravelly rise on a clay-limestone subsoil

GRAPE VARIETIES 80% Sémillon, 15% Sauvignon blanc, 5% Muscadelle

AGEING 16 to 18 months - New barrels: 100%

SECOND WINE Les Charmilles de La Tour Blanche

33210 Bommes
Tel.: +33 (0)5 57 98 02 73

Estate manager: Miguel Aguirre
Sales Director: Didier Fréchinet

tour-blanche@tour-blanche.com
www.tour-blanche.com

ChateauLaTourBlanche

latourblanche

Founded in the 17th century, Château La Tour Blanche is located in the commune of Bommes in the heart of the prestigious Sauternes appellation. In his will, the previous owner Daniel "Osiris" Iffla, left the estate to the French government in 1907, provided that a School of Viticulture and Oenology be created there.

The estate overlooks the Ciron river (a tributary of the Garonne), which is responsible for the unique micro climate conducive to the famous "noble rot".

Thanks to rigorous, environmentally-friendly management in the vineyard and cellar, Château La Tour Blanche was awarded High Environmental Value (HEV) and ISO 14001 certification. Cleverly combining traditional and modern methods has played an important role in encompassing the expertise required to make fine wines.

Château La Tour Blanche's style achieves a perfect balance between concentration and freshness, impressive finesse and elegance.

The Weekend des Grands Crus
Wine, gastronomic cuisine, leisure and relaxation!

Plunge into the universe of Grands Crus and create wonderful memories during an unforgettable weekend in Bordeaux!

Wine tasting

120 Bordeaux Grands Crus on the banks of the Garonne River: A wonderful opportunity to meet and discuss with representatives of each estate, who will be glad to pour you the most recent vintage of their wine in bottle as well as another wine of their choice.

Dinners

The chance to dine at the most prestigious Bordeaux châteaux alongside estate owners, where you can discover the wine and food combinations that have made the French cuisine and lifestyle so famous.

Tours

Visit the famous Bordeaux vineyards and enjoy lunch at a château thanks to bus tours leaving from Bordeaux.

The Union Cup

Lovers of fine wine and golf are invited to take part in a scramble golf tournament alongside château owners, followed by lunch at the Golf du Médoc.

The next Weekend des Grands Crus will take place
from the 18th to the 21st of June 2020

Contact details
grands.crus@ugcb.net
www.ugcb.net

"Bordeaux Grand Cru"

by Riedel

This glass, first created in 1959 by Claus Riedel in the handmade Sommelier collection, and by Georg Riedel in 1986 in its machine-made version Vinum, is not a design gimmick but a precision instrument, developed to highlight the unique characteristics of the great wines of Bordeaux. The large bowl brings out the full depth of contemporary wines made from Cabernet Sauvignon, Cabernet Franc and Merlot.

Modern vinification techniques enable wine-makers to concentrate the fruit to such an extent that young wines may seem one-dimensional, tannic and over-oaked if served in smaller glasses.

The Bordeaux Grand Cru glasses give breathing space to both young and more mature wines, unpacking the various layers of bouquet and delivering a full spectrum of aromas. On the palate, the texture of the wine - soft, silky, velvety - is intensified and the finish prolonged, gently blending acidity with supple, sweet tannins. This is a glass that showcases these majestically structured red wines in all their complexity and finesse.

RIEDEL

THE WINE GLASS COMPANY

www.riedel.com

PHOTOS

Château Angludet : © Lionel Simon / Château d'Armailhac : © Mathieu Anglada (left) - © Deepix (right) / Château Balestard La Tonnelle : © Vignobles Capdemourlin et Thierry Durandau (right) / Château Bastor Lamontagne : © Château Bastor Lamontagne / Château Batailley : © Château Batailley / Château Beaumont : © Château Beaumont / Château Beauregard : © Anaka / Château Beau-Séjour Bécot : © Château Beau-Séjour Bécot / Château Belgrave : © Twin Photographie / Château Berliquet : © Château Berliquet / Château Beychevelle : © Julie Rey / Château Le Bon Pasteur : © Château Le Bon Pasteur / Château Bouscaut : © Twin (left) - Château Bouscaut (right) / Château Branaire-Ducru : © Château Branaire-Ducru / Château Brane-Cantenac : © François Poincet - © Château Brane-Cantenac (portrait) / Château Broustet : © Gravier / Château La Cabanne : © Château La Cabanne / Château de Camensac : © Sabine Delcour / Château Canon : © Château Canon / Château Canon La Gaffelière : © François Poincet et Vinexia (middle) / Château Cantemerle : © Maud Bernos (left), Valérie Labadie (au middle), Vinexia (right) / Château Cantenac-Brown : © Château Cantenac-Brown / Château Cap de Mourlin : © Thierry Durandau (left and middle) - Château Cap de Mourlin (right) / Château Carbonnieux : © Deepix (portrait) - © Château Carbonnieux / Château Les Carmes Haut-Brion : © Philippe Labéguerie / Château de Chantegrive : © Château Chantegrive / Château Chasse Spleen : © Jean-Marc Palisse (portrait and photo by night) - © Felice Varini (barrel cellar) / Château Cheval Blanc : © Cécile Burban / Domaine de Chevalier : © Alain Benoit (left and middle) - © Jean-Pierre Lamarque (right) / Château Citran : © Château Citran / Château Clarke : © Olivier Seignette - © Taylor I Yandell / Château Clerc Milon : © Château Clerc Milon - © Mathieu Anglada / Château Clinet : © Anaka / Château La Conseillante : © Anaka (right and left) / Château Cos Labory : © Château Cos Labory : © Château Cos Labory / Château Coufran : © François Poincet / Château La Couspaude : © Vincent Paris - © Château La Couspaude / Château Coutet : © Gunter Vincente / Château La Croix de Gay : © Antoine Guilhem Ducléon (left and middle) - © Château La Croix de Gay (portrait) / Château Croizet-Bages : Château Croizet Bages / Château Dassault : © Serge Dulud / Château Dauzac : © Alex Cretey Systermans - Château Dauzac / Château Desmirail : © Gilles Arroyo - © Claude Lada (portrait) / Château Doisy Daëne : © Château Doisy Daëne / Château Doisy-Védrines : © Alain Benoît - © Château Doisy-Védrines / Château La Dominique : © Brice Braastadt - © Vinexia / Château Duhart-Milon : © F. Poincet / Château Durfort-Vivens : © Château Durfort-Vivens (middle) - © OneWineProduction - Raphaël Reynier / Château L'Évangile : © DBR (Lafite) / Château de Fargues : © Savinien Tonelli / Château Ferrande : © Castel / Château Ferrière : © Château Ferrière / Château de Fieuzal : © Château Fieuzal / Château-Figeac : © Hervé Lefebvre - Twin (right and left) - © Château-Figeac (middle) / Château Fonréaud : © Tran K. Thai / Château Fourcas Dupré : © Jean Lamarque / Château Fourcas Hosten : © Vinexia (left) - © Christel Jeanne (middle) - © Julie Rey (right) / Clos Fourtet : © Taylor I Yandell / Château de France : © Château de France / Château Franc Mayne : © Château Franc-Mayne / Château La Gaffelière : © Twin - Hervé Lefebvre / Château Gazin : © Sarah Mattews (left) - © Château Gazin : © François Poincet (right) / Château Giscours : © Vinexia (left) - © Château Giscours / Château Gloria : © Patrick Durand / Château Grand Mayne : © Pascal Rousse - © Mathieu Drouet - Agence Take a sip / Château Grand-Puy Ducasse : © Château Grand-Puy Ducasse - © Marie Astrid Jamoix (portrait) / Château Grand-Puy-Lacoste : © Serge Chapuis / Château Gruaud Larose : © Anaka (left) - © C. Goussard (middle) - © Château Gruaud Larose / Château Guiraud : © François Poincet (left) - © Château Guiraud / Château Haut-Bages Libéral : © Château Haut-Bages Libéral / Château Haut-Bailly : © Gérard Uféras - © Vinexia - © Clay MacLahan / Château Haut-Bergey : © Rodolphe Cellier - © Château Haut-Bergey / Clos Haut-Peyraguey : © Clos Haut Peyraguey / Château Kirwan : © Château Kirwan / Château Labégorce : © Julie Piatti (left) - © Château Labégorce / Château Lafaurie-Peyraguey : © Alain Benoît (right) - © Château Lafaurie Peyraguey / Château Lafon-Rochet : © Château Lafon-Rochet - ©Mathieu Garçon (middle) - © François Poincet (right) / Château Lagrange : © Deepix Studio / Château La Lagune : © Julie Rey / Château de Lamarque : © Château de Lamarque / Château Langoa Barton : © Château Langoa Barton - © Guy Charneau (middle) - © Furax (right) / Château Larcis Ducasse : © Gunther Vicente / Château Larmande : © Château Larmande - S. Klein (right) / Château Larrivet Haut-Brion : © Marianne Delleci (portrait) - © Vincent Bengold / Château Lascombes : © Château Lascombes / Château Latour-Martillac : © Saison d'Or - Mathieu Anglada / Château Léoville Barton : © Guy Charneau / Château Léoville Poyferré : © Jérôme Mondière (left and right) - © Benjamin Gay (portrait) / Château La Louvière : © Alain Benoît - Deepix - © Château La Louvière / Château Lynch-Bages : © Château Lynch-Bages / Château Lynch Moussas : © Château Lynch Moussas / Château Malartic-Lagravière : © M. Bonnie (left and right) - © Château Malartic Lagravière (portrait) / Château Malescot Saint-Exupéry : © Jérome Mondière - Lasuite Atelier / Château de Malle : © Château de Malle / Château Marquis de Terme : © Marquis de Terme / Château Maucaillou : © APC Viaud - © Château Maucaillou / Château Monbrison : © Ch. Monbrison / Château Mouton Rothschild : © Stefano Scata (left) - © Alain Benoît (middle) - Deepix (right) / Château Olivier : © Maria Alberola (middle and left) - © Gérard Uféras (right) / Château Ormes de Pez : © Château Ormes de Pez / Château Pape Clément : © Château Pape Clément / Château Pavie-Macquin : © OneWineProduction - Raphaël Reynier / Château Petit Village : © Château Petit-Village / Château de Pez : © Jean-Bernard Nadeau (portrait) - © Château de Pez / Château Phélan Ségur : © Château Phélan Ségur / Château Pichon Baron : © Château Pichon Baron / Château Pichon Longueville Comtesse de Lalande : © François Poincet - © Jean-Bernard Nadeau (portrait) / Château Picque Caillou : © François Poincet / Château La Pointe : © Château La Pointe / Château Poujeaux : © Taylor I Yandell / Château Prieuré Lichine : © Guy Charneau (left) - © Gunther Vicente (middle) - © Guy Charneau (right) / Château Rahoul : © Twin Photographie / Château Rauzan-Gassies : © Château Rauzan Gassies / Château Rauzan-Ségla : © Brice Braastad / Château de Rayne Vigneau : © François Poincet / Château Rieussec : © F. Poincet / Château Rouget : © Château Rouget / Château Saint-Pierre : © Patrick Durand / Château Sigalas-Rabaud : © Château Sigalas-Rabaud / Château Siran : © Maria Alberola (left) - © Anne Lanta (middle) - © Château Siran / Château Smith Haut Lafitte : © Château Smith Haut Lafitte - © Studio Deepix (portrait) / Château Soutard : © Tom Fecht - © Goussard (middle) - © Château Soutard / Château Suduiraut : © Ch. Suduiraut / Château Talbot : © Nicolas Seurot (middle) / Château du Tertre : © Vinexia (left and middle) - © Château du Tertre / Château La Tour Blanche : © Hervé Lefebvre – Studio Twin - © Vincent Bengold - © Mike Palace / Château La Tour Carnet : © Château La Tour Carnet / Château La Tour de By : © Château La Tour de By / Château La Tour Figeac : © Château La Tour Figeac / Château Troplong Mondot : © Cécile Perrinet Lhermitte / Château Trottevieille : © Château Trottevieille / Château Villemaurine : © Château Villemaurine / Château d'Yquem : © Uféras

INDEX
OF CRUS

General Remarks

The list of members belonging to the Union des Grands Crus dates from the 1st of February, 2019. The updated list can be found at www.ugcb.net.
Please note that there is no classification for the wines of Pomerol.
Furthermore, seeing as the size of the crop varies from one year to the next, the production figures cited in this guide are only an indication, and represent an average annual figure. They also only relate to the "grand vin".
Likewise, the surface area mentioned reflects not the total size of the estate, but the area under vine.

The guide is co-published by:

The Union des Grands Crus de Bordeaux
10, cours du XXX Juillet
33000 Bordeaux - France.
&
Éditions Féret

Editors
Union des Grands Crus de Bordeaux - President, Ronan Laborde - Manager, Grégory Citerneschi
Project Manager, Olivier Crombez

Coordination
Éditions Féret - Manager, Bruno Boidron - Assistant, Véronique Garrouste

Design
Laurence Maillet

Maps
Benoît France

Printed in March 2019 in the EU
Copyright March 2019

ISSN : 2116-5491
ISBN : 978-2-35156-235-2